SKILLS IN
RESISTANT
MATERIALS
TECHNOLOGY

Peter Gale

Heinemann

Heinemann Educational Publishers
Halley Court, Jordan Hill, Oxford OX2 8EJ
a division of Reed Educational & Professional Publishing Ltd

OXFORD MELBOURNE AUCKLAND
IBADAN JOHANNESBURG GABORONE
PORTSMOUTH NH (USA) CHICAGO BLANTYRE

Heinemann is a registered trademark of Reed Educational & Professional Publishing Ltd

First published 1999

03 02
10 9 8 7 6

British Library Cataloguing in Publication Data
A catalogue record for this book is available from the British Library

ISBN 0435 75044 5

Designed and typeset by Ken Vail Graphic Design, Cambridge
Illustrations by Nick Hawken, Gillian Martin, John Plumb, Simon Girling and Associates (Mike Lacey),
and Tokay Interactive Limited, Bicester, Oxon.
Cover illustration by Barry Atkinson
Cover design by Sarah Garbett
Printed and bound in Spain by Edlevives

Acknowledgements

The author would like to thank Alderbrook School, pupils and staff for their kind co-operation and support;
Zoe Collier and Sally Roundel for initial artwork; and Pamela Gale for invaluable support.

The publishers would like to thank the following for permission to reproduce photographs.

AKG London/Erich Lessing on page 6 (left and top right); Argos Distributors Ltd on page 14;
Gareth Boden on pages 4, 5, 16, 26, 32, 34, 35, 37, 39, 40, 41, 42, 43, 44, 45, 46 (left), 47 (left), 49, 50, 51, 53,
55, 56, 57, 66, 67, 68, 71 (left), 72, 73, 74, 75, 76, 79, 80, 81, 85, 91; Corbis on page 80 (bottom right);
Dorling Kindersley Ltd. Courtesy of the Museum of London on page 6 (bottom right);
Peter Gale on pages 18, 31, 38, 46 (right), 47 (top and bottom right), 50 (top right), 73 (bottom right);
Land Rover on pages 65 (bottom), 89; Last Resort Picture Library on pages 28, 36; MIRA on page 27;
Pictor Uniphoto on page 70; Powerstock Zefa on page 65 (top); Safeway on page 90;
Science Photo Library/Eye of Science on page 71 (right).

The publishers have made every effort to trace copyright holders. However, if any material has been
incorrectly acknowledged, we would be pleased to correct this at the earliest opportunity.

Contents

Safety

Safety is the first factor you should think about when designing and making things. In a workshop there are many safety hazards.

Safety guidelines

Here are some general rules to keep you and others safe:

If you don't know, ask!

When you are using a new tool or you are trying to do something for the first time, ask for advice. Not only will any safety issues be explained, but you will get a better quality of finish.

Do not rush

If you rush, you will spoil your work, as well as being a danger to yourself and others. This includes running and pushing past people.

Make sure your workspace is safe

Put tools away that you have finished using. Make sure you have not left items for people to trip over. Muddle is dangerous.

What hazards can you identify in this picture?

Always keep your hands away from sharp edges

One of the most common injuries when working with resistant materials is a minor cut from a knife or chisel. It can be tempting to hold a piece of wood and push a chisel towards your hand. If the chisel slips, there is a good chance that you will cut your fingers.

Sharp edge moving away from fingers – good!

Sharp edge moving towards fingers – dangerous!

Always wear the right safety equipment

An overall or apron is essential. It stops loose clothing from catching in machinery and keeps your clothes clean. Eye protection is absolutely essential when you are using any electrical machinery, heat or chemicals.

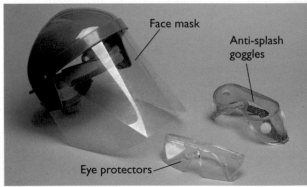

Face mask

Anti-splash goggles

Eye protectors

Different forms of eye protection

Do not go into a workshop without supervision

Teachers and supervisors are trained to make sure that you are safe in the workshop. They know what the risks are.

Make sure others are safe

When you are using machinery or sharp tools, make sure that others are standing out of the way.

Hazard and safety symbols: what they mean

Wear eye protection

Caution corrosive substance

Smoking and naked flames prohibited

First aid

Particular dangers in the workshop

Knife – always cut away from your hand. Use a safety ruler and cutting mat.

Chisel – do not use a blunt chisel. The finish you get will be poor and, because you have to use too much force to cut wood, it is dangerous. Carry chisels in a safe way. Your teacher will show you how. Always push the chisel away from you. Make sure that wood is held firmly.

Screwdriver – never force a screw. Always keep your hands away from the blade of the screwdriver in case it slips.

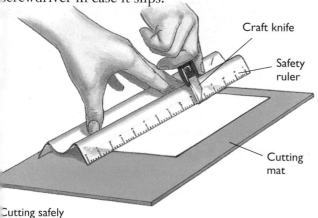
Craft knife

Safety ruler

Cutting mat

Cutting safely

Using a scroll saw. Fingers are kept out of the line of the saw cut

Scroll saw – do not force the saw to cut too quickly. Always keep your hands out of the way of the saw blade. Never push material into the blade with your hands in the line of the saw cut.

Power tools – make sure hair is tied back and all loose clothing is kept away from moving parts of machines. Wear eye protectors and an apron.

Polisher – always wear eye protection as objects can be thrown out of the polisher at high speed.

Heat treatment – wear eye protection, leather gauntlets and a leather apron. Be aware that anything in the heat treatment area may be hot. Do not pick objects up unless you know it is safe to do so.

If you or someone else is burnt ...

Put the burn under cold water and tell the teacher or supervisor immediately.

In case of electric shock ...

Do not touch the person. Switch off the power by pressing one of the safety stop buttons. Inform the teacher or supervisor immediately.

Safety is the responsibility of everyone. If you can't do it safely, don't do it.

To do

Make a poster for an activity or tool, to show how to do it or use it safely.

What is resistant materials technology?

Wood, metal and plastic are resistant materials. It is difficult to cut them and sharp-edged tools have to be used.

Resistant materials give us stiffness and strength in the objects we use. The bones in a skeleton give your body strength and shape. Metal, wood and plastic give shape to buildings, furniture and almost everything around you.

History

Since the very earliest times, when humans first became tool users, resistant materials have been used to change our world. Primitive people who lived around two million years ago started using stone tools to cut and scrape. This is perhaps the earliest example of resistant materials technology. The ability to use tools in a large variety of ways has helped us to evolve.

Making objects from plastic and metal involves complicated processes. It is easy to forget the thousands of years it has taken to develop the technology to produce and use these materials.

The first resistant material

Stone has been used for jewellery, weapons and tools almost as long as people have existed.

Flint tools were used for scraping and cutting in the Stone Age

Early metals

The first metal to be used by people was copper, about 10 000 BCE. Copper is a soft metal, so it was not very useful for weapons or tools, although examples of early copper axe heads have been found.

When tin and copper are heated together an **alloy** called bronze is made. Bronze is much harder than copper and was much more useful for tools and weapons. The earliest bronze items date from 4500 BCE.

A bronze dagger c. 1000 BCE

Iron and steel

The Iron Age came after the Bronze Age because the higher temperatures needed to make iron only became available with the development of the furnace. The earliest iron tools date from 3000 BCE. Steel is iron with small amounts of carbon in it. Steel is much **tougher** than iron.

An Iron Age dagger in a sheath c. 550 BCE

The Industrial Revolution

As coal mining became more organized and with the invention of the steam engine by James Watt in 1769, people were able to use the power of steam to do and make things they had only ever dreamed of before.

At this time the use of metals, particularly steel, became much more widespread and people's way of life was changed.

It was only in the twentieth century that we really started to understand how and why metals behave as they do. We can now make stainless steel as well as many other types of steel for a wide range of purposes.

The Plastic Age

The first plastics were developed at the end of the nineteenth century. However, it was not until the beginning of the twentieth century that they really started to become widespread, useful materials.

What about wood?

From well before the time when the first pieces of copper were found, wood was an important material for making almost everything. The feel and look of solid wood is still much appreciated. Even today it is one of the main materials used in building, because it is fairly easy to cut, it is quite strong and relatively light.

Where do resistant materials come from?

Wood

Wood comes from trees and, unlike all the other resistant materials, is a **renewable** resource. Trees can be planted to replace those felled for timber.

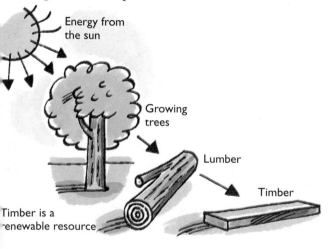

Energy from the sun

Growing trees

Lumber

Timber

Timber is a renewable resource

Plastic

Many plastics are made from **crude oil** which is brought up from below the ground. Oil is the remains of tiny animals that died millions of years ago and is not renewable.

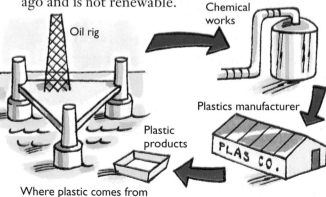

Oil rig

Chemical works

Plastics manufacturer

PLAS CO.

Plastic products

Where plastic comes from

Metals

Most metals come from **metal ores**, which are rocks found in the earth. Steel and iron are made from iron ore. Aluminium ore is called bauxite.

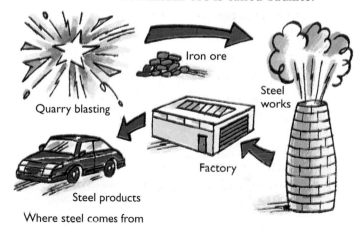

Iron ore

Quarry blasting

Steel works

Factory

Steel products

Where steel comes from

To do

Use the information in this section to make a time line. If you start with 4500 BCE and make 1cm represent 250 years, then the time line will fit on a piece of A3 paper held sideways.

Put dates and events on the line. Try to add drawings or pictures from magazines and from CD-ROMs to show when events happened. You can add extra dates, such as the building of Stonehenge or the discovery of America by Columbus.

Communication skills

It is very important to communicate your ideas effectively. For example, a large company that designs and makes children's toys will have many people working together. All these people need to communicate well with each other in order to make successful products.

Sketching

A **sketch** is a freehand drawing. It is quick but not very accurate. Sketches show the important features of a design. Notes are added to explain detail.

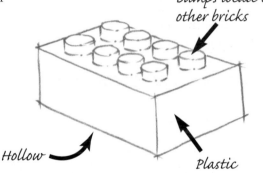

Bumps locate on other bricks

Hollow

Plastic

A sketch of a brick

Shading

Adding shading to a sketch can make it much easier to understand. Imagine light shining from one direction and then work out where the object is in shade.

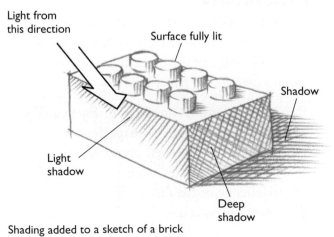

Light from this direction

Surface fully lit

Shadow

Light shadow

Deep shadow

Shading added to a sketch of a brick

Shading can also give objects a curved look. This needs practice but can really help to communicate your ideas.

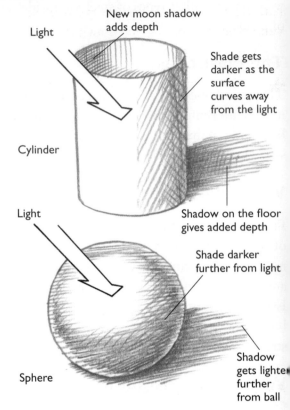

New moon shadow adds depth

Light

Shade gets darker as the surface curves away from the light

Cylinder

Light

Shadow on the floor gives added depth

Shade darker further from light

Shadow gets lighter further from ball

Sphere

Isometric drawing

An isometric drawing is a 3-D (three-dimensional) view of an object. This type of drawing is very clear and is accurate. However, there is some detail it cannot show.

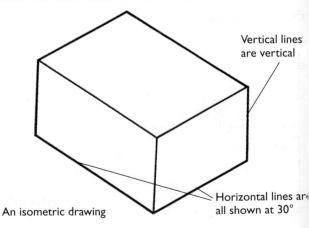

Vertical lines are vertical

An isometric drawing

Horizontal lines are all shown at 30°

Use of perspective

Perspective drawing is another 3-D view but is easier to understand than isometric drawing. Things that are further away in the drawing are shown smaller, to give the feeling of depth. This type of drawing cannot be to scale but gives a realistic view of an object. Perspective uses **vanishing points** to guide drawing.

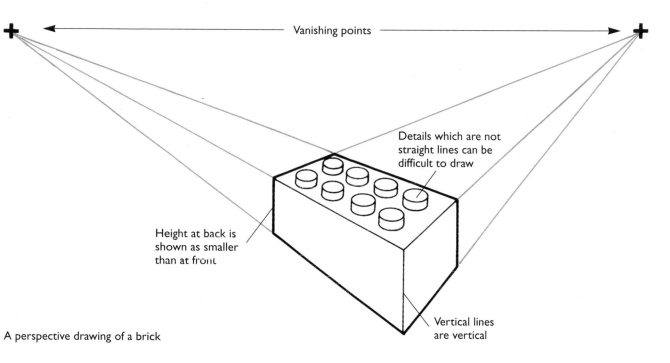

Vanishing points

Details which are not straight lines can be difficult to draw

Height at back is shown as smaller than at front

Vertical lines are vertical

A perspective drawing of a brick

Orthographic drawing

Orthographic drawings are working drawings and plans which are used for making things. An object is viewed from three different directions. The drawing is very precise and always to scale. All the detail of the shape and size of the object is shown.

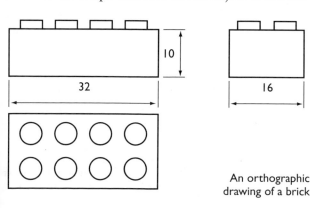

10

32

16

An orthographic drawing of a brick

To do

1 Make a quick sketch of a pencil case. Include some notes about materials you would use and the important features.

2 Look in magazines and newspapers to find drawings of objects using perspective. Try to find the vanishing points.

3 Make a sketch of a drinks can. Use shading to show the curved surface.

4 Draw a perspective view of a CD box.

The design process

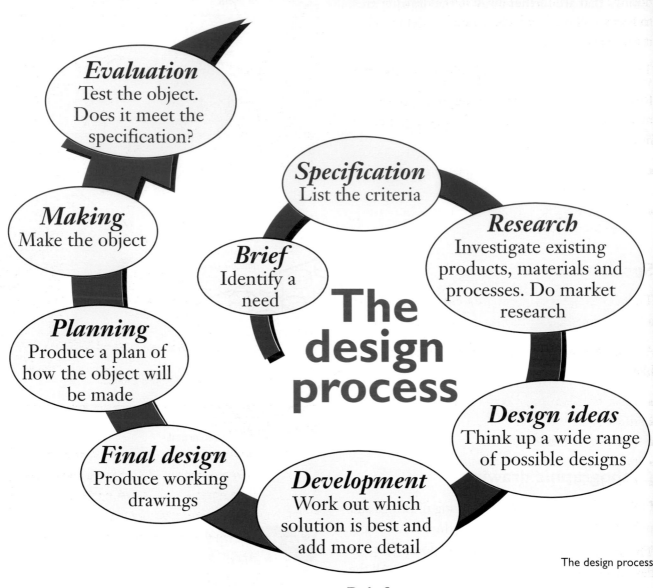

Evaluation
Test the object. Does it meet the specification?

Making
Make the object

Planning
Produce a plan of how the object will be made

Final design
Produce working drawings

Brief
Identify a need

Specification
List the criteria

The design process

Research
Investigate existing products, materials and processes. Do market research

Development
Work out which solution is best and add more detail

Design ideas
Think up a wide range of possible designs

The design process

Technology can solve problems that people face. Needs can be as small as having to hang washing or as large as sending someone to another planet.

The design **process** is very important in finding a successful solution to a problem and can be used in almost any situation.

Brief

The first stage of the design process is to work out exactly what the need is. This is called **generating a brief**. A brief is a statement about the task to be solved. It should be short and clear, for example:

Design and make a device to attach washing to a line.

In business a great deal of time and money is spent doing **market research.** This tells a company what sort of things people will buy.

Context

It is sometimes useful to write a short description of the **context**, or *why* there is a need for the product. This helps the designer to focus on exactly what the need is and how it can be satisfied.

The context for a clothes peg might look like this:

Research has shown that, although there are many clothes peg designs on the market, they are not perfect.

- Wooden pegs tend to go black with age and mark clothes.
- Plastic pegs crack after a short time because of ultraviolet rays from the sun.

Specification

The next stage is to write a **specification**. This is a list of **criteria** – or targets – which must be met.

A specification for a clothes peg might look like this:

- must hold washing on the line
- must resist wet conditions
- must resist ultraviolet rays
- must be quick and easy to use
- must be easy to store
- must be cheap enough to compete with existing products.

The specification will guide you towards the best design solution.

It is possible to change the design even as the object is being made. Changes to the design are called **modifications**. Reasons for the modifications can be explained in the **evaluation**.

Sometimes it is necessary to modify a design

Hint

People usually write the evaluation last and then can't remember all the changes they have made. Make notes as you go along. This will help you review your work later on.

To do

1 Write a specification for a door lock and key. Think about size, security, ease of use, cost, etc.

2 Imagine you work for a large pen manufacturing company. You have been told by the market research department that there is a need for a pen that writes under water, to be used by divers. Write a specification for the pen.

Project analysis

Brainstorming

This is a way of stimulating lots of ideas. The important rule for **brainstorming** is to note *all* ideas that come up, no matter how wrong they may seem. *Why?* – because what seems like a daft idea might make you or someone else think of something useful.

You can do a brainstorm by yourself, but it is often useful to get two or three other people to help you. The different ideas people have can trigger new ways of thinking.

It is good to group ideas and to make links using lines on the sheet like in the example below.

When you have finished brainstorming, organize the ideas and **analyse**, or study closely, the results to help you work out the most important parts of the project.

Hint

After a while come back to the brainstorm and have another look. Your brain will carry on working on the problem while you are doing something else.

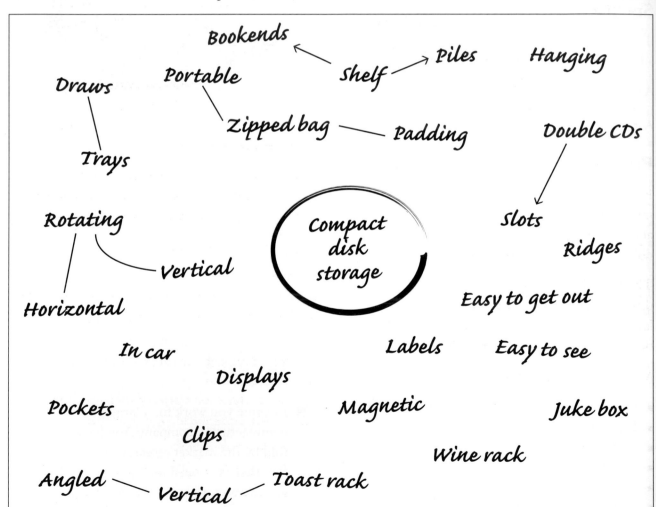

Brainstorming ideas

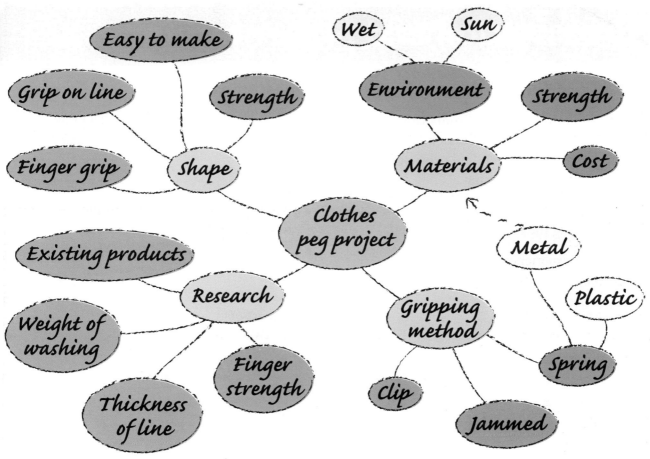

A spider diagram used in project analysis

Project analysis

Project analysis breaks a complicated problem into smaller bits, and helps you think more clearly about each part of the project. A good way of doing this is to draw a spider diagram (see above).

The analysis is in layers. When drawing your diagram, you could use colours to show these layers. Some parts of the project will link in to other parts. These links can be shown using lines.

More areas that could be in a project analysis

- safety
- legal issues
- environmental issues
- maintenance
- surface finish
- aesthetics (how will it look?)
- durability (how long will it last?).

Key features

Another way of analysing a project is to write down the **key features** of the design. These are the most important parts of the project.

Key features for a clothes peg:

- materials
- the way in which it holds the clothes on the line
- that it is easy and cheap to make.

To do

Do an analysis for a project to design and make a burglar alarm. Think about:

    a types of sound

    b types of burglar detector

    c ease of use by people who live in the house.

Information and presentation

Sources of information

Information can be gathered from many different places or **sources**. Some pieces of information are more useful than others and may not arrive in an organized or useful **format**.

Below are some sources of information you could use when doing the research for a project.

- your own experience
- experts
- magazines and catalogues
- the public – questionnaires
- interviews
- text books
- libraries
- CD-ROMs and computers
- companies
- existing products.

Information from computers

CD-ROMs and other computer sources allow you to find lots of information very quickly, but it is tempting just to print out all the information you find.

Here are some simple rules for using computers to gather information.

1 Always read the information to see if it is useful.
2 Read the text and write your own version.
3 Try to use information from more than one source.
   Use varied styles of presentation: text, pictures, clip-art, etc.

Questionnaires

Asking people questions is an excellent way of finding information, but be ready for their answers!

- Only ask questions that will give you useful information.
- Word the questions so that people are able to give answers that are clear and easy to record.
- You will need to record the answers quickly, so prepare an answer sheet.

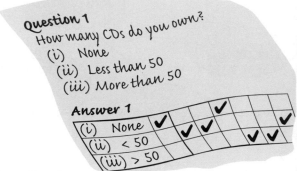

A questionnaire

Some questions will be facts about the person. These are usually easy to answer. Questions which ask for people's opinions can be difficult for them to answer, and their answers are harder to record. Try giving people choices by showing them pictures and asking them to choose their favourite.

Photographs of existing products

Analysing answers

Graphs and charts are good ways of showing the information you have gathered so you can analyse it carefully. Some ways of drawing graphs are more suitable for certain types of information than others. Choose the type of graph carefully, according to what you are recording.

Line graphs – these are used to show changes.

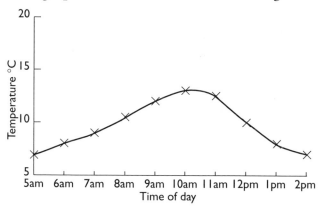

Bar charts (histograms) – show biggest and smallest.

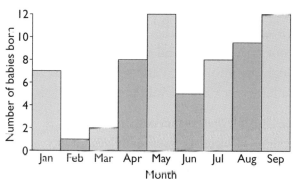

Computers can help you to present charts very quickly and with eye-catching shapes.

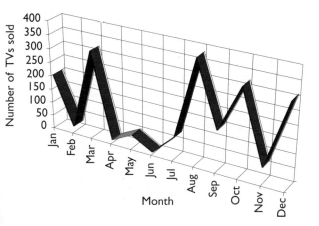

Pie charts – these show information in percentages.

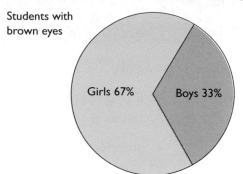

Scatter graphs – show links between answers to questions.

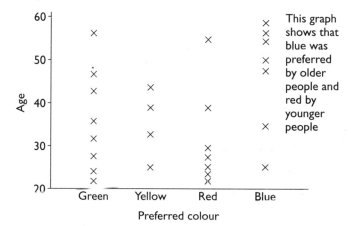

Graphs can be made more interesting by using shapes or pictograms.

Data presented in the theme of the information

To do

Draw a bar chart to show this information:

Out of 30 pupils in a class, 10 drink cola, 7 drink water, 5 drink milk, 5 drink fruit juice, 2 drink milk-shakes and 1 drinks coffee.

Using research

Planning your research

Research into a project needs to give you information about many areas. Some of these are:

- materials
- safety
- existing products
- processes
- costs
- legal issues.

The research part of the design process has five key stages:

1 Working out what you need to know
2 Gathering the information
3 Sorting and assessing the information
4 Presenting the information
5 Using the information.

Research case study (letter rack)

Stage 1 What to find out

To work out what information is needed, ask key questions about the product you are going to design. For a letter rack these could be:

- What size letters need to be held?
- How many letters need to be held?
- How will the letter rack work?
- What are existing letter racks like?
- Are there any similar products?

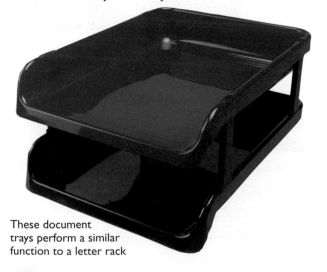

These document trays perform a similar function to a letter rack

Stage 2 Gathering information

Try to use several sources. The wider the variety of information, the better. Use cuttings from magazines or newspapers, visit shops and make notes on materials, sizes, costs and design.

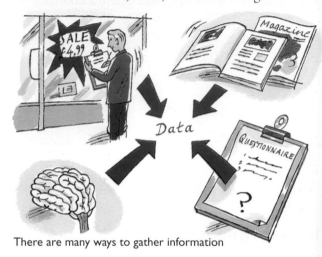

There are many ways to gather information

Stage 3 Sorting and assessing information

Not everything you gather will be useful, and it will not arrive in a logical order. You need to sift through the information and sort it into sections. For a letter rack these could include:

- measurements of standard envelopes
- designs of letter racks already available
- materials and prices
- where letter racks are placed.

'If that's a standard size then I'm a poodle!'

Stage 4 Presenting information

Group and present the information clearly so that the important points are highlighted and it looks interesting to read. To do this you will need to add written notes and headings.

A pupil's research into designing a letter rack

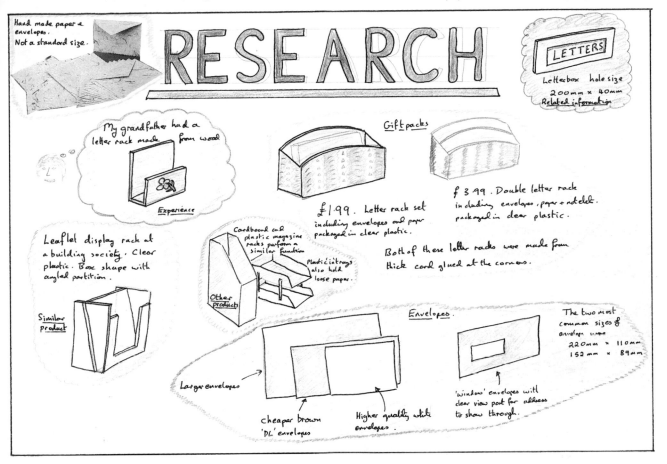

Stage 5 Using information

Good research will present you with conflicting ideas. You will have to make decisions based on the information about which are good ones to use. Write a summary of the findings of each section of your research and show clearly what you have discovered. Sometimes your research will lead you to ask further questions and this will mean more research.

The reason for researching is to find out as much as possible to help you design and make a product. Make sure that you explain in detail how you have used the information to help with your designs, and include this as part of the development of your designs.

To do

1. Make a list of the areas you would need to research in order to make a bookshelf for a young child.

2. On one piece of A3 paper present some information you have gathered about the books that a young child might have.

3. Write down a summary of the information you have gathered and identify the important points you will need to consider when generating design ideas for the bookshelf.

17

Disassembly, product analysis and mass production

Disassembly

Disassembly is:

- taking something apart to see how it is made
- looking at something and working out why it was made that way.

Disassembling a clothes peg

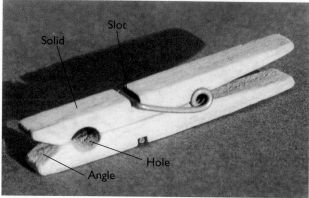

A wooden clothes peg

Why is a wooden clothes peg made like it is?

A plastic clothes peg does the same job and this means that it is very similar in design.

Notice how similar the shapes and sizes of the two pegs are. Where the shapes are the same, there must be a good reason.

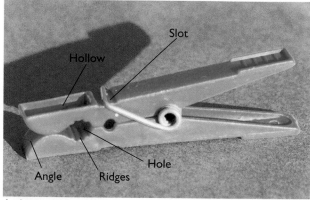

A plastic clothes peg

Why make a peg from plastic rather than wood?

Why was this peg made from plastic?

- Plastic is waterproof and does not go mouldy.
- Plastic is a very cheap material which can be moulded accurately.
- Wood is a natural material and can have splits or knots which would ruin the peg.

Why are the designs of the pegs different?

Unlike the wooden peg, the plastic peg has:

- ridges on the gripping part to make the naturally smooth surface of the peg jaws hold the clothes better
- hollows to reduce weight and use less material
- ridges which hold the two parts of the peg in position. Wooden pegs cannot have these and sometimes fall apart
- ridges inside some of the hollows to give extra strength.

How was the peg made?

The plastic peg has been injection moulded. The point where the plastic was injected is a small dent in the jaws. Injection moulding is a very fast, reliable method of production, allowing great accuracy and quite complicated shapes to be made.

Although the shapes of the pegs are nearly the same, the plastic material allows for improvements in the design of the peg which would not have been possible using wood.

Which products to disassemble

If you are making something like a coat hook, for example, it would be useful to find a range of coat hooks and disassemble them.

You could also disassemble things that have been made using similar processes and materials. This would help you to analyse the product.

Product analysis

Product analysis is thinking about an existing product and trying to work out why it was designed this way. This helps you design your own.

Some questions to help analyse a product

1 Why has it been made out of this material?
2 Are there any expensive or difficult processes involved in making it?
3 How has the object been designed to be made in quantity?
4 What does it do?
5 Are there any weak points to the design?
6 Are there any other materials or processes you could use to improve the product?
7 Who would buy this product?
8 Why is it this colour?
9 How was it mass produced?

Mass production

Mass production is making things in large quantities.

There are two types of mass production, **continuous** and **batch**.

Continuous production
Objects are made one after another.

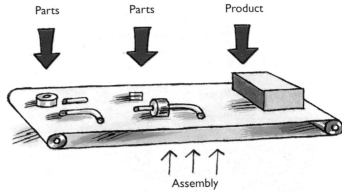

Continuous production

Batch production
A number of objects are made together.

Batch production

To do

1 Plastic pegs are injection moulded. Try to work out how the wooden peg was made in large quantities. Write a brief account of the production process.

2 Disassemble a plastic comb. How was it made? What are the key features of the design?

3 Disassemble a pencil. How was it made? Briefly describe each step of the making process.

4 Produce a display to show disassembly of a plastic fizzy drinks bottle. Include a product analysis.

Design ideas

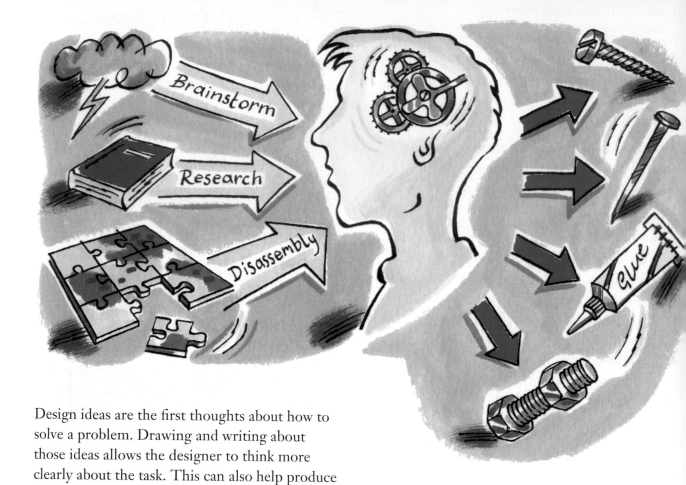

Use research, disassembly and brainstorming to help generate a wide variety of ideas

Design ideas are the first thoughts about how to solve a problem. Drawing and writing about those ideas allows the designer to think more clearly about the task. This can also help produce even more ideas.

Sketches can save having to write down your ideas. Pictures cut from magazines or catalogues can also show your design thinking.

An aid to thinking

Generating a number of design ideas helps you to consider a variety of solutions and think more clearly about ways of solving a brief.

There is always more than one solution to a problem. Your first idea is not always the best one.

Most ideas come from existing designs or personal experiences.

Choosing a design

Consider each idea to decide which ones are worth developing. You need some criteria to make choices, for example:

- are the materials suitable
- what are the costs
- how difficult is it to make
- will people buy it
- how well does it meet the specification?

Communicating ideas

- Use rough sketches with notes to explain your ideas.
- Don't put too much detail in at this stage. It is better to have quite a few different ideas that are only partly thought out.
- Think about individual parts of the design as well as the whole solution.
- Make sure that a range of ideas is generated.

- Don't reject a design just because it doesn't seem as good as the others. It might have a good feature which can be used later.
- The sketches don't have to be to scale or of a very good quality, as long as they communicate the idea.
- Use a blow-up of a feature to show more detail.

The drawings below show some design ideas for a shelf.

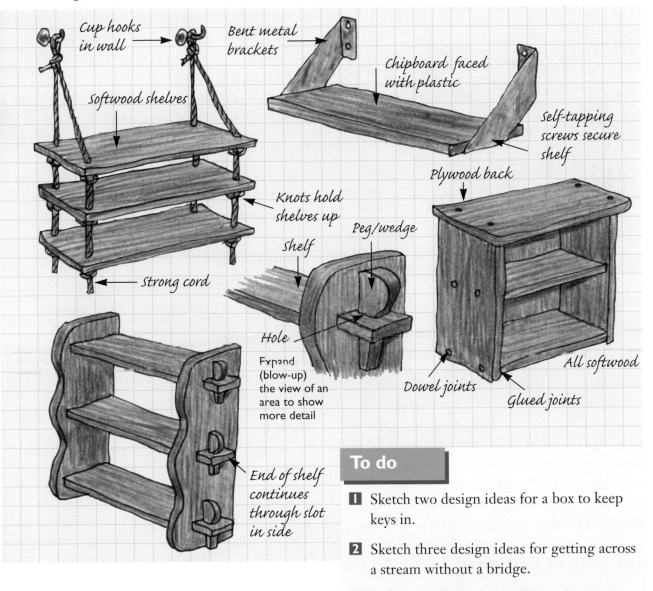

Cup hooks in wall

Bent metal brackets

Chipboard faced with plastic

Softwood shelves

Self-tapping screws secure shelf

Plywood back

Knots hold shelves up

Peg/wedge

shelf

Strong cord

Hole

Expand (blow-up) the view of an area to show more detail

Dowel joints

All softwood

Glued joints

End of shelf continues through slot in side

To do

1. Sketch two design ideas for a box to keep keys in.

2. Sketch three design ideas for getting across a stream without a bridge.

3. Sketch five design ideas for keeping next door's dog out of your garden.

Development and final design

Developing an idea

To arrive at the final design, the best features from the various design ideas are developed.

Below is how the design ideas from page 21 for a set of shelves could be developed. An **isometric** drawing has been used to give more accuracy. Notes are added to show fine detail.

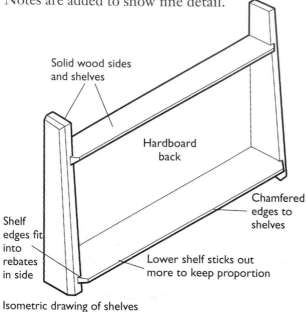

Solid wood sides and shelves

Hardboard back

Chamfered edges to shelves

Shelf edges fit into rebates in side

Lower shelf sticks out more to keep proportion

Isometric drawing of shelves

Notice how ideas from several of the sketches on page 21 have been used to improve the basic design.

As the design develops, different ideas or new ways of making the product may come up. It is good to include these in your design even though the design ideas stage has been completed. Modifications may even be made during the making process, as you find that one method or part of the design doesn't work as well as you had thought it would.

Justifying design ideas

In school and in business it is important to **justify** design decisions, explaining why choices have been made. This is part of the development process.

Why this design?

Each part of the design should be explained. In the shelf example:

- the shelves are of different depths to take different sizes of books
- the angled front edge of the sides removes the squareness of the initial designs
- the rebates which hold the ends of the shelves give greater strength than dowel joints
- hardboard at the back prevents books from falling off the back of the shelf
- the bottom edges of the shelf are **chamfered** to make the shelves look less clumpy.

And so on …

The shape of the shelves has been decided. The next stage is to make final decisions about sizes, positions and the making process.

Final design

The final design is a set of drawings and information about materials and processes.

The drawings

The drawings should be **orthographic** to show details of shape and size. These are always drawn to scale (see opposite).

Parts list

A list of all the parts that will go to make the shelves must be completed (see opposite).

The parts list shows the type of material, the sizes and the quantity of each part that is needed. The parts list is a vital piece of paper. It tells the people responsible for buying and cutting material in the company or school exactly what is required.

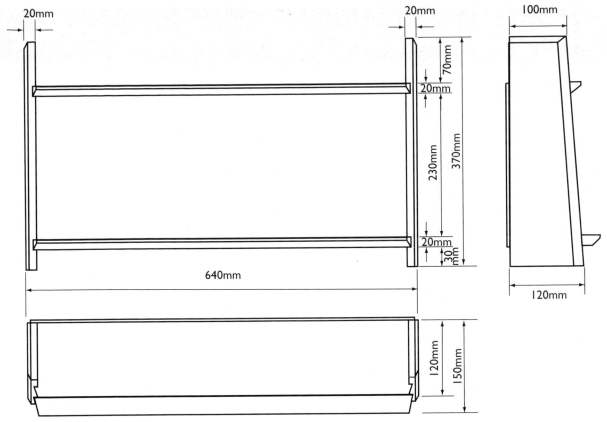

Orthographic drawing of shelves

Parts list					
Part name	Material	L *Length (mm)*	W *Width (mm)*	T *Thickness (mm)*	QTY
Side	Wood	370	120	20	2
Top shelf	Wood	640	120	20	1
Bottom shelf	Wood	640	150	20	1
Back	Hardboard	250	640	3	1

Parts list for shelves

To do

Draw up parts lists for the following items: wooden clothes peg; wooden table; drawer. You can use real objects to give you measurements or you can invent your own.

Flow chart

The order in which tasks should be done is important. A flow chart is useful for this (see page 24).

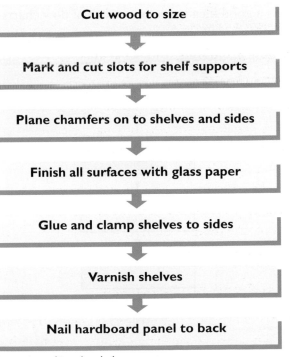

Cut wood to size

Mark and cut slots for shelf supports

Plane chamfers on to shelves and sides

Finish all surfaces with glass paper

Glue and clamp shelves to sides

Varnish shelves

Nail hardboard panel to back

Stages in making the shelves

Planning for success and flow charts

Flow charts

Flow charts are a way of clearly showing the order in which things happen. They have special shapes to show types of activities, like the symbols on a map.

Flow chart symbols

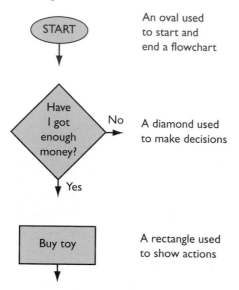

An oval used to start and end a flowchart

A diamond used to make decisions

A rectangle used to show actions

It is a good idea to use a number of flow charts to describe small sections of a process. For example, nailing a joint might look like this:

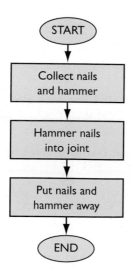

Process for nailing a joint

Flow charts become more complicated when decisions have to be made. This makes the flow chart split or loop as in the example below, where a box is being varnished.

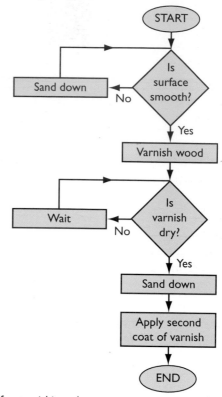

Process for varnishing a box

Flow charts in action

Flow charts can also describe things that happen, for example, closing a lift door.

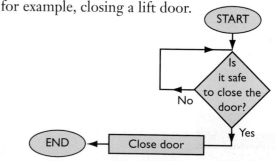

Closing a lift door

When doing a project, you can use one flow chart to show the whole of the project and several others to show the details of making the object.

Planning and the use of a time chart

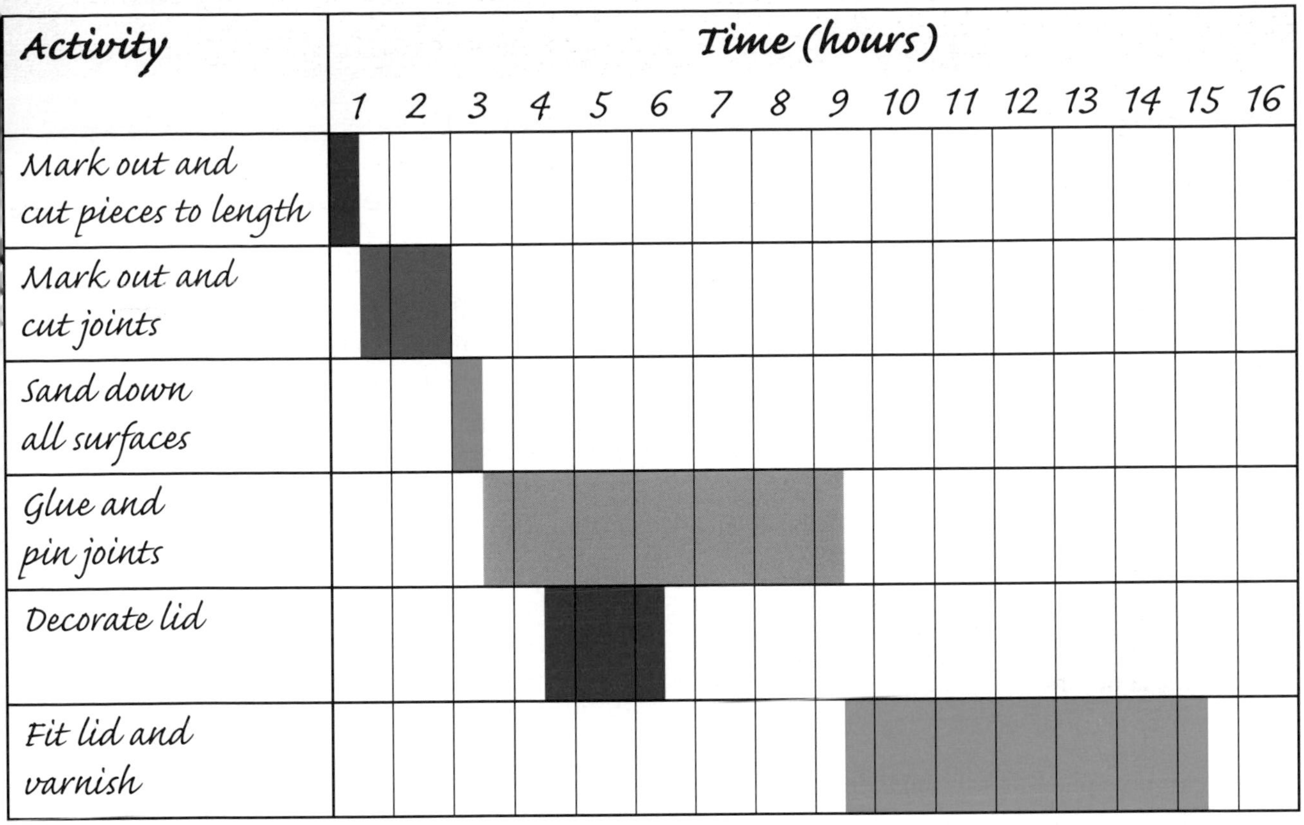

Activity
Time (hours)
1 2 3 4 5 6 7 8 9 10 11 12 13 14 15 16
Mark out and cut pieces to length
Mark out and cut joints
Sand down all surfaces
Glue and pin joints
Decorate lid
Fit lid and varnish
An example of a time chart

Planning is simply thinking ahead. People plan all the time, like making sure there is enough milk for breakfast in the fridge before the shops shut.

Planning a technology project takes practice and needs to be written down so that it can be studied and improved. There are many ways of showing planning, but one simple method is to use a time chart as shown above.

The chart above shows the activities in a list on the left-hand side and the time in hours across the top. The time each activity takes is shown by the length of each box.

Hint

Look for the things that are going to take a long time and plan to do something else meanwhile, so you don't waste time.

Notice how some boxes overlap. This shows that two activities can be happening at the same time. In this case, the decoration for the lid of the box is being painted while the glue on the joints is drying.

To do

1. Draw a flow chart for brushing your teeth.
2. Draw a time chart for getting from your front door to the school door in the morning.
3. Draw a flow chart for crossing the road.
4. Draw a time chart for making a cup of coffee. (*What could you do while the kettle boils?*)
5. Draw a flow chart for a person using a lift.

Quality control, quality assurance and testing

Quality control

Quality control is a system of testing to see if a product meets certain standards. The purpose of quality control is to check that an item has been made correctly.

Testing is an important part of the **manufacturing** or making process. Sometimes every object is tested, for example, for size and weight. This is very expensive and takes time. Most products are batch tested, which means that a few items are taken at regular intervals and tested. This is far cheaper to do, but some faulty products may go undetected.

Testing can take place at any stage during the making process, and when a complicated system like a car is made, many thousands of tests must be carried out before the vehicle is finished.

Simple products need fewer tests. A washer is usually stamped out of a strip of steel. After a few million washers have been made, testing might show that the edges are rough or the hole in the middle is too small. This is probably because the tool being used is becoming worn and needs changing.

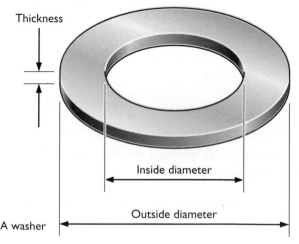

A washer

What is good enough?

Objects are tested to check that they meet a set standard or specification. No object can be made totally accurately, so a **tolerance** is used. The tolerance is the maximum and minimum measurement something is allowed to be.

If a washer, for example, should have a diameter of 15mm with a tolerance of + or – 0.01mm, then the washer can be between 14.99mm and 15.01mm. It would fail the test if it had a diameter which fell outside these maximum and minimum sizes.

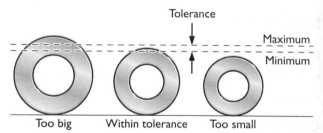

Testing the diameters of washers

For some products, for instance engine parts, the tolerance is very small. This means that the part must be made very accurately and this, of course, makes it more expensive to produce.

Using a micrometer to check the diameter of a rod

Quality assurance

There is another way in which manufacturing companies try to make sure that their products are up to standard. **Quality assurance** is the system that a manufacturer uses to ensure that items will be made correctly.

There are many areas of quality assurance, these include:

- materials – checking to see that the supplier provides good quality materials
- processes – making sure that the machinery is operating properly
- equipment – regular servicing and sharpening of tools
- training – training people to do their jobs correctly.

Summary

Quality control – checks made after production to make sure that the product reaches certain standards.

Quality assurance – the systems used before and during manufacture to make sure that products are made correctly.

Testing

There are two main types of testing:

Destructive – when metal or plastic objects are made they often need to be tested for strength. Sometimes this means the object needs to be tested until it breaks. This is called destructive testing.

For example, car manufacturers are required by law to crash-test their vehicles to see how they would behave in a collision. Although it seems a waste, it is important to drive a number of brand new cars into a concrete block.

Non-destructive – these are tests which do not damage the product. For example, locks are tested to make sure the key works before they are sold, without damaging them.

Destructive testing of a car

Questions

1. Which of the following are areas of quality control and which are to do with quality assurance?
   a   measuring the length of a screw
   b   training
   c   maintaining cleanliness in a paint spray area
   d   setting off a driver's air bag.

2. How do you think quality assurance can help cut down the costs of production in a large business?

3. How could you test a set of moulded chess pieces?

Natural resources and the environment

Renewable materials

Replanting to ensure future supply of wood

Wood is a renewable material which can be replaced within a few years.

Trees can be grown in a **managed forest**. This means that for every tree cut down a new tree is planted. In this way the resource is renewed.

Non-renewable resources

Most of the materials we use, apart from wood, are non-renewable. Metals come from rocks which contain a **metal ore**, such as iron ore, or aluminium ore which is called bauxite. Once the ore has been taken from the ground it cannot be replaced.

The **raw material** for making plastics is oil. Oil is the remains of the tiny creatures that lived in the sea millions of years ago. Once oil has been taken from the ground it cannot be renewed.

Some materials are more difficult to find than others and so cost more. Gold, silver and platinum are called precious metals because they are rare. Aluminium is quite easy to find, but it is difficult to turn it from ore to metal and so it is more expensive than steel.

Recycling

Recycling waste materials

Many towns have bottle banks, skips for waste paper and card and aluminium can recycling centres. As the cost of raw materials rises, it is becoming more **economical** to save used materials and use them again. This is called recycling.

This symbol is found on many packages. It means that the materials in the packaging can be recycled.

Recycling symbol

People sometimes use separate bins for all their rubbish, so that they can recycle plastic, paper, metal, glass, etc.

Interesting fact

The amount of energy which falls on the Earth from the Sun in one day is more than the energy used by all the people on the planet in a year.

Energy

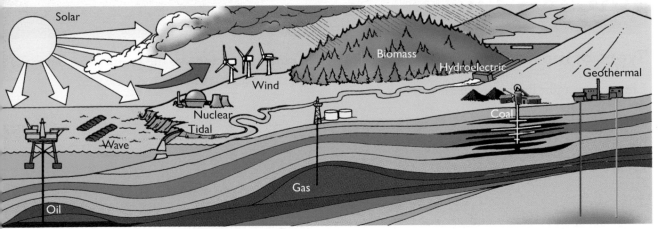

Energy sources

Non-renewable (capital) energy sources

The main energy sources that we use are oil, coal and gas. These are called fossil fuels, because they are formed from the dead bodies of animals and plants that lived millions of years ago. Unfortunately these are not renewable. They are called **capital energy sources**.

Nuclear power has become more common in the last thirty years or so, but the waste material is very dangerous and needs to be safely stored for thousands of years.

Renewable energy sources

Because the Earth's main energy sources are not renewable and will therefore one day run out, we have to use alternative renewable sources. These include:

- hydroelectric – electricity from moving water
- biomass – plants burned to produce heat
- tidal power – electricity from moving tides
- wind power – electricity from wind turbines
- geothermal – heat from underground
- solar power – from the Sun.

Pollution

Many waste products from the manufacturing industry can be harmful to the environment. Some chemicals kill fish in rivers and lakes and change the way that plants and animals grow.

People are becoming more aware of the problem of pollution and are making an effort to take more care of their environment.

Some packaging is **biodegradable** which means that it will rot after a few years. On the other hand, many of the plastics that we threw away in the past, rather than recycled, will lie unchanged in the ground for thousands of years because they do not break down quickly over time.

The environment and money

Not polluting the environment and using recycled materials is often expensive. If we are to protect our environment, we need to be prepared to pay more for the things we use. We must be more careful about how we use them and how we get rid of them afterwards.

To do

Find out more about capital energy resources. In a small group, prepare a three-minute presentation for the rest of your class. Your teacher will outline the area of research for your group. You can use poetry, jokes, music, drawings, etc. to help make the presentation interesting.

Movement

Types of movement

Linear – straight line movement.

Reciprocal – backwards and forwards in a straight line.

Rotary – moving in a circle.

Oscillating – backwards and forwards in an arc.

Most moving systems change one type of movement to another. There are some important moving systems which have special names.

Rack and pinion – the rotary motion of the **pinion** is turned into **linear** motion of the **rack**.

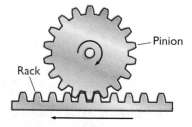

Threads – the thread turns and moves slowly through the cramp.

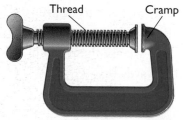

Worm drives – each turn of the **worm drive** moves the gear one tooth only. The gear turns much more slowly than the worm drive.

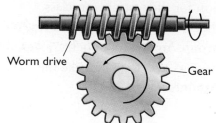

Crank and slider – as the **crank** turns once, the slider moves backwards and forwards.

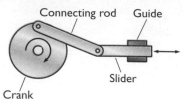

Cam and follower – as the **cam** turns the follower moves up and down.

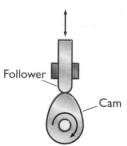

Changing the direction of movement

Reversing

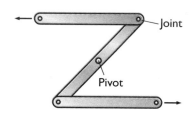

Bell crank – the movement changes direction by 90°.

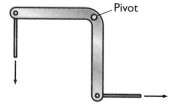

Amplifying and reducing – the size of the movement is changed because the pivot is not in the middle.

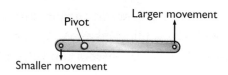

Gears

Gears can be used to change the speed and force of a movement.

A simple gear train

A compound gear train

Pulleys and belts

Pulleys can change the size of a movement as well as transferring it to another place.

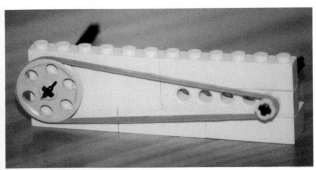

Belt and pulley system

To do

1 Make a cardboard model of the reversing mechanism. What happens when the pivot is not in the middle of the central beam? Try to explain your observations.

Gear or pulley?

Gears and pulleys seem to do very similar jobs, so why should you choose one rather than the other?

- Gears have cogs. The number of teeth on a cog can be counted which makes the motion of gears very accurate. Clocks and sewing machines need gears to keep the movements in time.
- Gears do not slip, so they can be used to transfer very large forces.
- Gears are expensive to make and they need to be accurately placed so that the teeth mesh, or fit together, properly.
- Pulleys are cheap to make and, because the belts used with them are stretchy, they do not need to be accurately spaced.
- Pulleys cannot be used to transfer large forces as the belt may slip.

Bearings and friction

Friction occurs when two surfaces rub against each other. A lubricant like oil can reduce friction by keeping surfaces apart.

Magnified view of rough surfaces touching

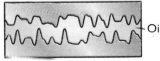

Surfaces kept apart by oil

A bearing allows two surfaces to slide past each other with very little friction.

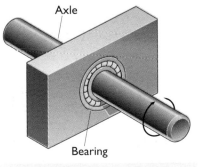

Axle

Bearing

2 Make a cardboard model of a crank and slider. Investigate the effect of changing the size of the crank. Try to explain your observations.

Metals and their properties

Metal	Cost	Strength	Weight	Rust and corrosion	Examples of uses
Steel	Cheap	Extremely strong	Heavy	Rusts easily	Bridges, buildings, ships, cars, reinforcements in concrete
Aluminium	Expensive	Fairly strong	Light	Does not rust	Aeroplanes, saucepans
Brass	Medium cost	Strong	Medium	Does not rust	Nameplates, bearings, handles
Copper	Expensive	Easily stretched	Medium	Surface corrosion	Electrical wires, roofs
Gold	Very expensive	Easily bent	Very heavy	Does not rust	Jewellery, electrical contacts

Properties of different metals

Metals are very useful materials to make things from. They are strong, can be moulded and keep their shape.

The two most commonly used metals are steel and aluminium.

Steel

Steel is iron with a little bit of carbon in it. The carbon makes it much stronger and tougher.

Stainless steel contains chromium. This stops the steel rusting. Cutlery is made from stainless steel. Stainless steel is much more expensive than ordinary steel.

Steel is strong and quite cheap. This means that it is very useful in many applications. The main problem with it is that it rusts when in contact with the air.

Stopping rust

Rust is the product of a chemical reaction between the air and water and steel. If steel can be kept apart from air, then it will not rust. There are a number of ways of protecting steel from rusting.

Painting – a layer of paint protects steel from rusting and improves the look of the finished object. However, painting is quite expensive and takes time. Paint can be easily scratched, which means that air can get to the steel and it will rust where the scratch is.

Galvanizing – the galvanizing process coats steel with large crystals of zinc. This is a quick and cheap method of protecting steel from corrosion but does not look as good as paint.

Galvanized steel

Oil and grease – oil and grease protect steel from air, but they are messy and dust sticks to the surface. Steel is coated in oil to prevent it from rusting whilst it is being stored.

Aluminium		Steel	
Property	Effect	Property	Effect
Light	Useful for making aircraft	Heavy	Only useful when weight is not too important
Does not rust	Surface goes dull	Rusts	Needs to be protected
Less strong than steel	Much easier to bend into shape than steel	Very strong	Can be used in bridges, building, etc.
Easier to cut than steel	Quicker and easier to machine than steel	Hard to cut	Needs heavy machinery to form it
Has a low melting point	Easier to cast than steel	Has a high melting point	Needs special equipment for casting
Fairly expensive	Product costs more	Cheap	Widely used
Difficult to paint	Surface needs special treatment before painting	Quite easy to paint	Widely used

A quick guide to the properties of steel and aluminium (what they are like)

Aluminium

Aluminium is widely used because it is light and does not rust. It is easier to cut than steel because it is much softer. Aluminium also has a lower melting point, which makes it easier to melt and pour into a mould.

Some cars have steel frames but aluminium body panels. The steel gives strength and the aluminium panels will not rust.

Look at the table above to see how steel compares to aluminium.

Copper

Copper is a soft metal. It is easy to shape but too weak for construction. Copper is an excellent **conductor** of electricity and heat. Its main use is in electric cables.

Copper is quite expensive. Some top quality saucepans have copper bases to spread the heat quickly. Some roofs are covered in copper sheet. It is quite easy to solder copper to give waterproof joints. When exposed to rain, it will go green but it will not rust away.

Brass

Brass is an alloy of copper and zinc. The surface of brass becomes dull after a few days but can easily be polished to give a bright yellow surface. Because it is attractive and does not rust, it is used for nameplates and door handles. Brass screws are used in boat building where steel ones would rust.

Brass is harder than aluminium but softer than steel and it can be worked fairly easily. It is much more expensive than steel, so it is used for small items which need to look good.

Questions

1. Why are some expensive saucepans made with copper?

2. Brass is not usually painted. Why not?

3. Why is copper used for making water tanks and pipes?

4. Why are ships made from steel plates even though steel rusts badly in salt water?

During the twentieth century, the manufacturing industry changed enormously as plastics developed. Many objects which used to be made from steel or wood are now made cheaper and better using plastic materials.

The main advantages of plastic as a construction material are:

- it is easily moulded
- it is water resistant
- it does not rust
- plastics have an enormous range of properties
- it is very strong for its weight
- plastics are very cheap.

Now and then

Look at the example of coat-hangers to see how things have changed. They used to be all made from solid wood, with a bent wire hook. The wood was strong enough to support the weight of clothes and the smooth surface protected them from damage. Plastic coat-hangers have now largely replaced wooden ones.

Plastic can be moulded, so there is very little waste, and the variety of shapes possible is much greater. The surface of the plastic can be made smooth or ridged at the time of moulding, so there is no need for expensive varnishing.

Plastic and wooden coathangers

Another example of change is that plastic has replaced rubber for use as an **insulating** material in domestic wiring. It has all the good qualities of rubber but does not perish.

Types of plastic

Acrylic – comes in a wide range of colours and has a very shiny surface. It can be drilled, sawn and filed like a very soft metal. If heated it can be easily bent, but it does not mould very well without special equipment. Acrylic is brittle and so care must be taken when it is being worked to avoid cracking.

Nylon – has a surface which gives very low friction, so it is often used for nuts, bolts and washers. Nylon is not brittle and can be machined like a metal although it is quite soft.

Nylon nut and bolt

Polystyrene – comes in two types. Ordinary polystyrene is a hard material used for vacuum forming. Expanded polystyrene is used as packaging inside boxes. Because this material is soft, light and strong, it protects delicate equipment during transport.

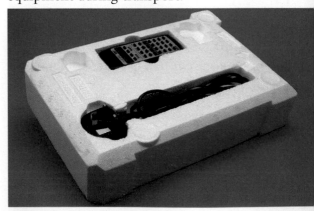

Expanded polystyrene packaging

Polypropylene – is a light plastic which is used in ropes and food containers, because it does not break when it is bent.

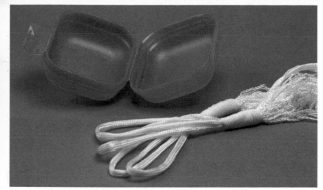

Polypropylene container and rope

PVC – or polyvinyl chloride, can be manufactured as a hard or soft plastic and so has a very wide range of uses from clothes to plumbing.

PVC products

Plastics are sometimes used with other materials to improve their performance. GRP, or glass reinforced plastic, is used for making large rigid structures like garage doors, aeroplanes and boat hulls. The combination of strength with toughness as well as lightness means it is cheap to produce.

To do

Collect samples of as many products made from plastic as you can. Try to identify what type they are as well as the reasons why that particular material has been used for this product.

Thermoplastics

Thermoplastics are a group of plastics which can be softened by heating. They harden again when cooled. These plastics are useful for moulding, but cannot be used where the material will become hot.

Thermoplastics melt in the heat

Thermosets

Thermosets can be heat moulded, but once they have set, they will not go soft when heated again. This makes them very useful for products that must withstand heat, but they cannot be bent into shape from flat sheets in the workshop.

Questions

1 Why are casings for most electrical equipment made from plastic rather than metal?

2 Explain why a designer might choose polypropylene as the material for a food container.

3 What are the advantages of vacuum-formed plastic food containers over cardboard or tinned packaging?

4 Why do you think nylon is often used to hold wheel axles on pushchairs?

Wood is a natural material. It has a range of different properties depending on which tree the wood comes from.

Wood has a **grain** and this makes it different from other resistant materials. It is stronger along the grain than across the grain. Wood grain is formed as the tree grows. Each year another line in the grain is added.

There are two main types of wood: hard and soft. Hardwoods look better than softwoods because of their colour and grain.

Hardwoods

These come from trees that have broad leaves which fall off in autumn (**deciduous trees**). Hardwoods usually have a close grain and are hard to saw.

Oak produces hardwood

Examples of hardwoods are oak, ash, beech, mahogany and birch.

Interesting fact

Ebony is nearly black and is so hard and dense that it sinks in water.
Balsa is nearly white and is one of the lightest and softest woods in the world. Both are hardwoods!

Balsa and ebony

Softwoods

These come from conifers (trees with cones). Their leaves are usually like needles and do not fall off in autumn, so they are called evergreen.

Pine produces softwood

Softwoods tend to have a wider grain than hardwoods and they are easier to saw. Because softwoods grow faster than hardwoods, it does not take as long for the trees to mature. This makes softwood much cheaper than hardwood. The surface finish on softwoods is not as good as hardwoods. Examples of softwoods are pine, deal, yew and larch.

Softwood	Hardwood
Fairly cheap	Expensive
Easy to cut	Hard to cut
Pale colour	Many colours
Coarse grain	Fine grain
Fairly light	Usually heavy
Good surface	Excellent surface

The properties of softwood and hardwood

Mouldings

Mouldings are lengths of wood that have been shaped. These are useful for finishing the edge of a piece of work and for making picture frames.

Dowel is a cylindrical moulding made from solid wood. There are many uses for dowel, from fixing joints to broom handles.

Wooden mouldings

Wood-based materials

Because wood is a natural material, it can **warp**. Wood warps as it dries and bends or twists. It may also have splits or knots which spoil the piece of wood. When planks of wood are sawn, sawdust and small useless pieces of wood are produced. These are processed and used to make **manufactured boards**. These are sheets of material that can be used for making things.

Hardboard

Hardboard is made from small fibres of wood, compressed to form a thin sheet. One side is treated to make it smooth and shiny, the other side is rough. It is very cheap and is often used to cover the backs of cupboards and the bottoms of drawers. Hardboard is quite weak and needs a frame to give it strength.

Medium density fibreboard (MDF)

MDF or medium density fibreboard is a very useful and strong material, often made into furniture. It is made of resin and small wood fibres. It can be sawn like softwood and is very easy to shape into curves because it has no grain. Care needs to be taken with the edges of MDF boards as they can easily be damaged.

Plywood

Plywood is made from very thin sheets of solid wood, glued together. There is always an odd number of layers and the grains of the layers are at right angles to each other. Plywood is a very strong material and it is a fairly cheap way of covering large areas. There are several types, suitable for different uses. For example, exterior plywood (for use outside) is held together with waterproof glue whilst flooring grade plywood is much thicker as it has to be able to take great weight.

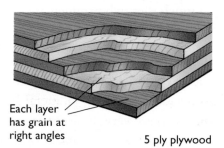

Each layer has grain at right angles

5 ply plywood

Chipboard

Chipboard is made by gluing large fibres of wood together to form a board. It is a very cheap material which is used to make kitchen furniture, work surfaces and floors. Chipboard is usually quite thick to give it strength. When used for making kitchen cabinets and work surfaces, it has a plastic coating glued to it to make it waterproof.

Fixing manufactured board

Manufactured boards are made from fibres or layers of wood glued together. They are not as strong as softwood or hardwood and normal woodscrews will pull out quite easily. Therefore special screws and fixings are sold for fixing these boards.

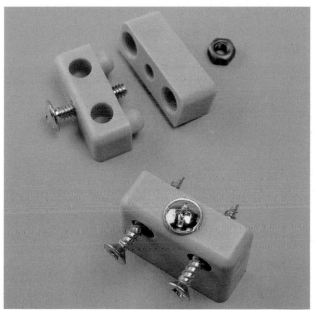

Screw blocks for joining chipboard

To do

1. Find samples of different types of manufactured board. Make a labelled chart to show what they look like and what they are used for.

2. Take samples of wood and manufactured boards and place them in water for a day. Make notes on the damage done by the water.

Materials for the job

Getting it right

Choosing the right material is a very important part of design. Some of the things that you should consider when choosing a material are:

Cost – is there a cheaper material?
Availability – can you get the material?
Properties – does it meet the specifications?
Durability – will it last?
Maintenance – can it be repaired or repainted?

The material you choose will affect the processes you can use and the design of the object. Here are two similar designs of corkscrew using different materials.

Wood and metal corkscrews

The choice of materials is in three stages:

1 What must the material do? (specification)
2 What materials might be suitable? (research)
3 On balance, which is the best material for the job? (decision)

To help with the final stage, it can be useful to use a score card. Each of the criteria for choosing the material is given a maximum mark and each material is scored on how well it meets the criteria.

Arriving at a decision

A tool box can be made out of metal, plastic or wood. The three main criteria are strength, weight and cost. The table below is a score chart to see which material should be used in this particular case.

Each of the criteria used has a maximum mark which shows how important that criteria is. In this case, weight is less important than either strength or cost. Weight is scored out of ten whilst the others are scored out of twenty.

Material	Strength	Criteria Weight	Low cost	Total score
Max mark	20	10	20	50
Wood	15	10	8	33
Plastic	7	7	12	26
Steel	18	8	5	31

A decision-making chart for which material to use

Here, the wood solution has scored best. This type of decision-making chart can also be used at other stages in the design process.

Material properties

The secret of good design is to make the best use of the properties of a material, and to choose the right material for the job it has to do. Sometimes the material being used will influence the design so much that two products made to do the same job will look very different.

To understand the link between the material and the way it is used we will look at the design of tool boxes made using wood, metal and plastic. These materials are very different from each other in the way they are worked, and how they can be used.

Tool box in wood

Softwood is used for the ends and the sides to give strength. It is also fairly cheap to buy.

Plywood is used for the base as it is cheaper than softwood. Hardboard could be used but it might not be strong enough for heavy tools.

Dowel is used for the handle as this gives a comfortable grip for carrying without the need for time-consuming shaping of a handle.

Softwood is used for the main partition in the base, to add strength to the design and to give a good material for the threads of the screws to cut into.

Tool box in metal

Steel is used for the main structure of the box as it is strong, cheaper than any other metal and can easily be bent into the right shapes.

Aluminium rivets are used for the hinges as these are more easily shaped than steel.

Tool box in plastic

The main body of the box is made using plastic which is injection moulded. This gives a strong and accurate structure. The accuracy of the injection moulding process is important for lining up the hinges.

The compartments in the lid are again injection moulded, but this time using a clear plastic. The lift-out compartment tray is also injection moulded using transparent plastic.

To do

Develop a score chart to help you decide on the best material for making a garden fencepost. You should consider concrete, wood and metal. Criteria should include cost, ease of transport, ease of use and how long it will last (durability).

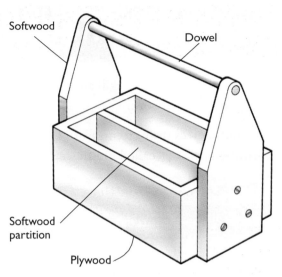

Wooden tool box

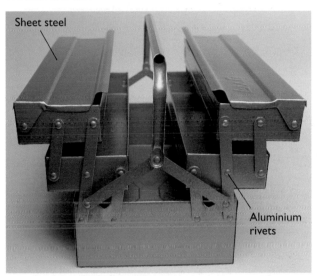

Steel tool box

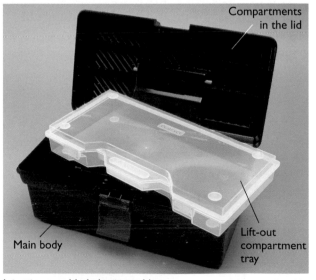

Injection moulded plastic tool box

Measuring and marking out

Accuracy in measuring is a key skill and is essential to good quality work.

Always use millimetres (mm) to measure things. This measuring system is called metric.

Metric conversion chart		
millimetres	centimetres	metres
1000	100	1
100	10	0.1
10	1	0.01
1	0.1	0.001

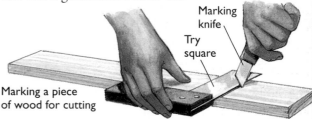

1cm
10mm

Steel rule

Wood

The basic tools for measuring and marking out wood are:

Steel rule

Pencil

Marking knife

Try square

The basic tools for measuring and marking wood

Marking wood for cutting

Sometimes wood needs to be **planed** flat and square before you can start. To mark out a piece of wood for cutting to length, measure the length needed from the end of the piece of wood with a steel rule and make a small mark with a pencil. Use a try square and marking knife to mark a line at right angles all the way round the wood. You can mark the knife cut with a pencil afterwards to make it easier to see. The marking knife cuts across the wood fibres and this helps to give the saw cut a good finish later on.

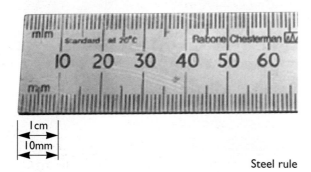

Marking knife

Try square

Marking a piece of wood for cutting

Marking hole centres in wood

Use a steel rule and a pencil to mark a small cross to show where a hole is to be drilled. Push a bradawl into the wood surface. The bradawl will leave a small hole which helps to keep the drill bit in the right place.

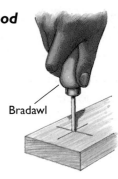

Bradawl

Marking a hole centre in wood

Marking gauge

A marking gauge helps to mark depths along the edges of wood. It is one of the more difficult marking tools to use and will take some practice. Its sharp point is dragged to leave a mark.

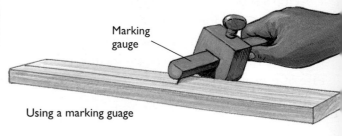

Marking gauge

Using a marking guage

Metal

The basic tools for measuring and marking out metal are:

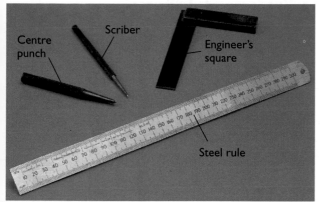

The basic tools for measuring and marking metal

Steel should be prepared with marking blue to make scratches easier to see. Use a steel rule and a scriber in the same way as you would use a pencil, to scratch a mark on the metal surface. Use an engineer's square to mark lines at right angles to straight edges.

Marking the centre of holes on metal

To mark hole centres for drilling, use a steel rule and scriber, to mark a small cross. Then place a centre punch at the centre of the cross. Give the head of the centre punch one sharp tap with a hammer. The dent made by the centre punch will help keep the drill in the right place when the hole is drilled.

Marking out for metal has to be very accurate indeed, so take care to get it right.

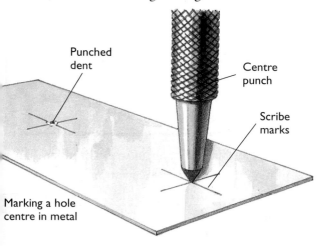

Marking a hole centre in metal

Plastic

Plastic is difficult to mark accurately. If you scratch the surface, the scratch can be difficult to remove afterwards. The simplest way is to use a fine permanent pen. If the plastic has a protective film on it, leave it on. Use a try square or engineer's square and a steel rule in the same way as with steel or wood.

Many projects using plastic have shapes. A cardboard **template** is a good way of marking the curves of a design on to the plastic accurately.

Marking bends on plastic

One of the common processes used with plastic is heat bending. Make sure you know which lines are for bending and which ones are for cutting. Remember the bending process is often inaccurate.

Marking holes on plastic

Because the drilling of plastic is different from wood or metal, do not mark just the centre of the hole. It is best to use a large cross and a ring. The drill bit will fit inside the ring.

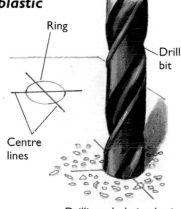

Drilling a hole in plastic

Questions

1 Measure the height of this page. Write down the length in millimetres, centimetres and metres.

2 Why is a small dent made on the surface of steel before drilling?

3 Why should you use a marking knife to mark lines on wood?

4 Why should you use a steel rule for marking out rather than a plastic or wooden one?

Tools for wood, metal and plastic

Care and safety

Most tools used for metal, plastic and wood have sharp edges. Care needs to be taken to protect people from injury and to protect the sharp edges of the tools from being damaged.

Saws

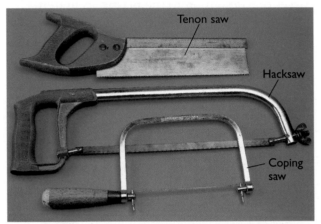

Different types of saw

Tenon saw – used for cutting wood in straight lines. The tenon saw works best if you use the whole length of the blade, which should always be vertical. If you start the cut in the right place and the blade is kept straight, then the cut will usually be good.

Hacksaw – used to cut metal. Its teeth are too coarse for plastic and it leaves a messy finish if used on wood. A junior hacksaw is good for small cuts in metal, cutting wood mouldings, dowel and plastics.

Coping saws – these are very useful, as a range of blades can be fitted for different uses. They are best for cutting curves as the blade is very thin and can turn corners. It is important to keep the blade at right angles to the wood all the time and not to force it to cut too fast.

Drill bits and drills

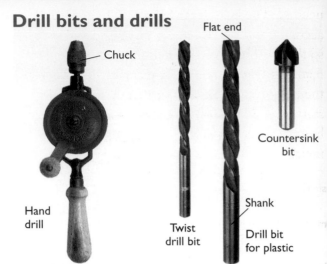

The two types of drill bits you will use are a twist drill bit and a countersink bit. For wood and metal the twist drill bit has a pointed sharp end, to help guide it into the material. When drilling plastic, use a twist drill bit with a flat end so that it scrapes the plastic rather than cuts it. This reduces the risk of cracking and splitting.

The countersink bit makes a cone-shaped hole, which lets the heads of screws fit level with the surface of the material.

Hand drills

A hand drill is useful for small holes and countersinking. To tighten the chuck, hold it still and turn the drill handle clockwise. To get the bit out of the chuck, hold the chuck still and turn the handle anti-clockwise.

Pillar drills

> *Very great care must be taken when using any power tool. Always make sure that you consult your teacher before starting to drill.*

For metal and larger holes in wood, a pillar drill is a much quicker and more accurate tool than a hand drill. Pillar drills have a depth gauge so that the drill stops at the right depth.

Hammers

Hammers have different shapes for different uses. For small nails and pins, a small hammer is needed. The head is fairly light to help with accuracy and the flat face of the hammer is small so that you can hit the small pins without damaging the surrounding material. The back of the hammer head is thin so that the pin can be started while being held between fingers. For larger nails, use a larger hammer. For bending metal or riveting, use a heavy hammer.

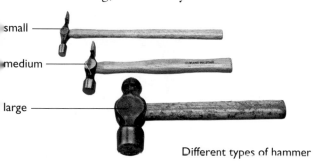

small

medium

large

Different types of hammer

Holding materials

If you use the correct holding tool, it will make the job much easier, and give a better result. Always hold the work low in the vice (particularly plastic) to reduce vibration.

Vices

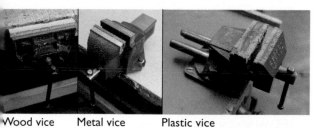

Wood vice   Metal vice   Plastic vice

Vices which hold wood are large and have wooden jaws to protect the surface of the material. Holding metal needs more force, so a metal vice is needed, which has metal jaws. The inside of the jaws have a pattern to grip the metal and stop it slipping. Plastic needs a lighter vice with plastic jaws to stop the material being damaged.

A bench hook is a quick way to hold pieces of wood. Your weight holds the wood in place.

Chisels

These are probably the most dangerous hand tools in a workshop. There are two main safety rules for chisels.

1 When using a chisel the sharp edge should always move away from your body, including both hands.
2 Carry a chisel in a safe way. Your teacher will show you how.

There are many kinds of chisel but the most common is the bevel-edged chisel.

The main use of a chisel is to remove small pieces of wood that cannot be cut with a saw.

Cutting sheets

> One of the most frequent injuries in a workshop is a small cut from a craft knife. Be careful and always cut away from your fingers and body.

For straight edges use a safety rule. This keeps your fingers above the level of the knife blade. Use a cutting mat under the material. This protects the table top from cuts and helps prevent slipping.

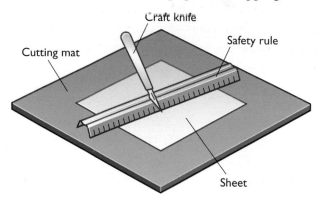

Craft knife

Safety rule

Cutting mat

Sheet

To do

Make a list of all the tools you have used. Describe what each tool is for and note whether you have mastered the use of it, whether you need more practice or have difficulty using it.

Practical skills

Standing

Standing correctly whilst working with tools is very important. If you stand with your feet in the wrong place, you will have great difficulty in getting a good quality finish.

Stand with your feet apart. This makes you stable and lets you push and pull tools more easily.

If you are right-handed, stand with your left foot forward and your right foot further back and at right angles. If you are left-handed, stand with your right foot forward and your left foot further back and at right angles. Having the back foot angled moves your hips and lets your arm move straight backwards and forwards in a straight line.

The correct way to stand

Hammering

Hold the hammer at the end of the shaft, not near the head. Make sure the face of the hammer is flat when it hits the head of a nail. If it is at an angle the nail will bend.

Small nails or pins need to be started by tapping them into the wood. Use the back end of the hammer which is thin and will slip between your fingers. Gently tap the head of the pin until it stays in the wood on its own. Now use the front end of the hammer to drive the pin in.

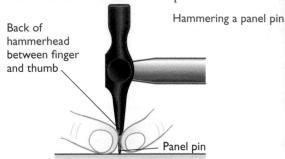

Back of hammerhead between finger and thumb

Hammering a panel pin

Panel pin

Gluing

Wood glue needs several hours to set. The glue should be rubbed into both surfaces to be glued, and the surfaces should be held firmly together. Use scrap wood to protect the surface of the wood from being marked by the cramps.

G cramp

Scrapwood protects surfaces from bruising

Waste wood packing to protect wood from metal cramp

Sash cramp

Different types of cramp

Drilling

The most difficult thing about using a hand drill is keeping the drill at right angles to the material. It is worth asking a friend to check that the drill is in the right position.

To make sure that you drill the hole to the right depth, stick a piece of masking tape to the drill bit at the depth you want. When the masking tape reaches the material, you know you are deep enough.

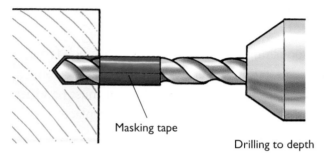

Masking tape

Drilling to depth

Filling

Gaps are sometimes left where a joint has not been cut very accurately or there is a hole in the wood for some reason. If the gap is left, it will look unattractive, and can make finishing with varnish or paint difficult. The gap can be filled using wood filler or a mixture of sawdust and glue.

Sawdust from the same type of wood as you are filling will give a good colour match and is very cheap. When the filler is dry, it can be sanded down just like solid wood. Sanding can actually help to disguise the filled gap.

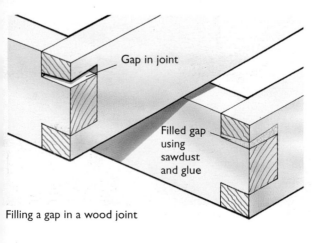

Gap in joint

Filled gap using sawdust and glue

Filling a gap in a wood joint

Filing

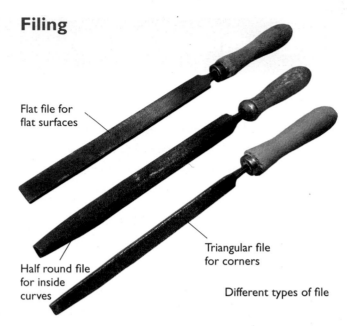

Flat file for flat surfaces

Triangular file for corners

Half round file for inside curves

Different types of file

When filing metal or plastic, if possible try to file along the edge. This will give a flatter finish and be far less noisy. Use the correct file for the shape.

Flat files have a 'safe edge' on one side – one edge of the file has no teeth. When you file into the corner of a piece of metal or plastic, the safe edge should rub against the surface you do not want to file. If the wrong edge is used, the teeth will cut into the surface and spoil the finish.

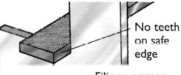

No teeth on safe edge

Filing a corner

Draw filing

To get a very smooth finish, hold the file at right angles to the direction it is moving. The teeth will scrape a much smaller amount of material, and the surface will be quite smooth.

To do

Make a display showing the tools and processes used to produce a shiny finish on plastic and metal. Include samples of the surface finish at each stage.

Power tools

Hand-held power tools

Many homes have electric sanders and drills and they are very useful. Hand-held power tools are usually less powerful than floor- or bench-mounted machines, but they can still be dangerous if handled incorrectly.

There are some simple rules for using power tools:

1 Always wear eye protectors.
2 Wear an apron to keep your clothes clean and prevent loose clothing from being tangled in the tool.
3 Make sure that electric leads are out of the way and will not be tripped over.
4 Never force the tool or try to use it incorrectly.
5 Check with your teacher before using a power tool for the first time.

Pupils in schools must not use routers or circular saws.

Electric sanders

Electric sanders can quickly smooth large surfaces. Move the sander backwards and forwards in the same direction as the grain. Use a gentle pressure. Do not be tempted to lean on the sander to make it sand more quickly.

Using an electric sander to smooth a surface

Workshop machines

These are more powerful than hand-held power tools and you will need special training before using them.

Polishing

Polishing metal or plastic by hand using metal polish is very time-consuming.

A polishing machine or **buffer** is a much faster way of gaining a very good mirror surface on plastic or metal. Safety equipment must be worn and the correct guards should be in place.

> *These machines are very powerful and loose clothing could catch in the machine and drag you in. An apron must be worn and tied securely at the back. Make sure that you wear eye protection.*

Hold the work firmly and gently let the cloth wheel of the polisher rub the surface. Do not force the material into the wheel to get a faster finish.

Use the lower front part of the wheel. Any corners which could catch in the wheel should face away from you.

> *Caution – metal can get hot when being polished.*

A buffer

Metal and wood lathes

To use these you will need special training. Metal lathes are very powerful indeed and should not be used without supervision.

Pillar drills

If you have been trained to use them correctly, these machines are excellent for drilling holes accurately in plastic, metal and wood.

Protective clothing must be worn as well as eye protectors. Loose clothing or hair can be caught in the spinning chuck so it is very important to make sure that all clothing is kept well away from the machine and that hair is tied back.

There will always be a guard around the drill bit and chuck. Make sure that it is down when you are drilling.

To hold material when using a pillar drill, use a machine vice. Make sure that the material is held firmly.

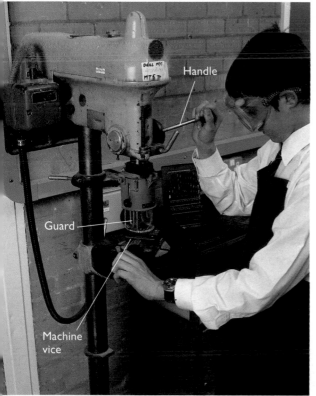

Using a pillar drill

The chuck holds the drill bit on the shank. To tighten the chuck, use a chuck key. Always be sure to remove the chuck key from the chuck as soon as you have used it. If the drill is started with the chuck key still in, it will be thrown across the room at high speed.

The chuck holds the drill bit on the shank

To drill holes of a certain depth, use the depth stop. Move the end of the drill bit down to the required depth and then screw the depth stop to stop it going down any further.

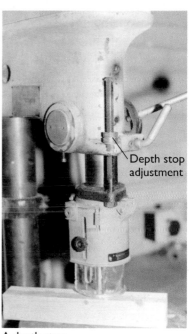

A depth stop

To do

1. Use drawings and notes to explain how to drill using a pillar drill. Remember to include the safety precautions needed when using power tools.

2. Design a set of rules that could be hung next to the pillar drill to remind people about safety.

Permanent joints

A permanent joint is one where two pieces of material are held together and cannot be pulled apart. Permanent joints are usually cheaper and stronger than temporary joints.

Metals

There are several ways in which metals can be permanently joined:

Welding – steel can be welded either by using a very hot flame (gas welding), or by using large electric currents to heat a small area (spot weld). Gas welding is very strong but needs skill and is expensive. Spot welding is very quick and cheap, but is not as strong as gas welding and is only suitable for sheet steel. (See page 65 for more information on welding.)

The body panels which fit on to a car chassis are spot welded. Different types of welding are used for greater strength in other parts of the car's structure.

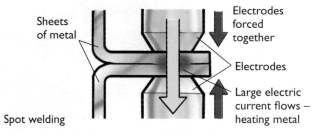

Spot welding

Brazing – this is similar to welding but the temperatures needed are much lower. The steel pieces to be joined are held close together. **Flux** is placed on and around the join area. The area is heated until it is red hot and a metal brazing rod is melted into the joint. The liquid metal runs between the pieces of steel and bonds to them. When the steel cools, the melted metal sets and the join is complete. The joint is quite strong and neat.

Soldering – this is quite similar to brazing but at much lower temperatures and the joint is much weaker.

Riveting – rivets are made of solid metal, usually aluminium or steel. Rivets made of aluminium are much easier to fit because it is softer. Steel rivets give a stronger joint. There are two types of rivet:

- Countersunk head rivets fit into shaped holes so that when the rivet is hammered, it takes up the shape of the hole it is in and can be filed **flush** (level) with the surface.

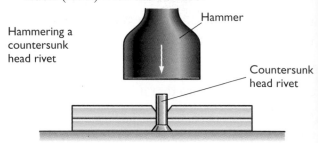

Hammering a countersunk head rivet

- Round headed rivets are fitted using hardened steel tools. The holes in the tools are shaped to mould heads on to the rivets.

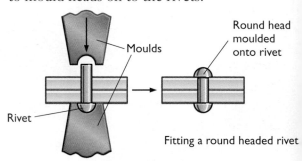

Fitting a round headed rivet

Pop rivets – a special tool is used to put a shaped piece of aluminium through a hole in sheet material. Pop rivets are not very strong and the heads stick out from the surface, but they are a quick and easy way to join sheets.

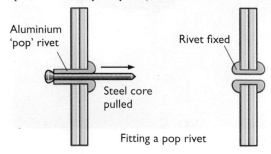

Fitting a pop rivet

Interference fit (friction fit)

If a metal rod is forced into a hole which is just big enough, friction will hold the two parts together. Sometimes the outer piece of metal is heated. This makes the hole in it bigger. When it is cooled again it contracts and grips the rod.

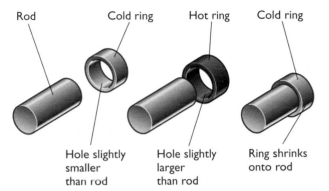

Fitting a ring on a metal rod

Plastic

Plastic is usually welded or glued to make a permanent joint.

Plastic welding

Plastic has a low melting point, so it is quite easy to weld. Plastic bags are made in this way. Welding plastic is very quick and cheap.

Plastic gluing

There are many types of glue that can be used on plastic, but many are dangerous and also give off unpleasant or toxic fumes. Gluing plastic with the right glue can give very good joints, but safety precautions must be taken.

Harmful

Highly flammable

Always read the safety instructions on labels

NO SMOKING
No Naked Flames

Wood

One of the oldest methods of joining wood is the peg. A joint is cut, and the two pieces of wood are fitted together. A hole is then drilled and a peg is hammered into the hole which holds the two pieces together.

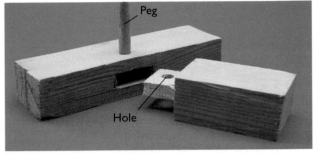

Peg joint

Gluing wood

Wood is often glued to make a permanent joint. The bigger the surface that is glued, the stronger the joint. If the surfaces are held together for a few hours, the joint is often stronger than the wood itself.

Glued joints can be held together with clamps, nails or screws whilst the glue dries. (See pages 62–3 for more information on wood joints.)

Halving joint

To do

Take several pieces of wood which are the same size and shape. Using various types of glue, stick samples of them together and leave to dry. When the glues are set, test each one to see which glue is strongest. You could try wood glue, contact adhesive, PVA and glue gun.

Temporary joints

A temporary joint is two pieces of material held together which can be taken apart. Temporary joints are usually more expensive and weaker than permanent joints.

Metal and plastic

The most common way of joining metal is to use a nut and bolt. The proper name for a bolt is a machine screw. The nut holds the bolt in place. The big advantage of using nuts and bolts to hold pieces of material together is that they can quickly be taken apart for **maintenance** and repair. Brake blocks on bicycles are a good example.

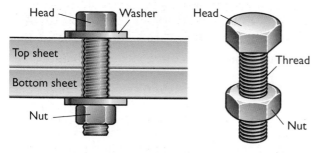

Joining metal using a nut and bolt

A nut and bolt

Washers, nuts and bolts

Washers are rings of metal or plastic used with nuts and bolts. They help protect surfaces and stop nuts coming undone.

Nuts and bolts come in many shapes and sizes. The thicker the bolt, the stronger it is, but it will also be more expensive. For a company using one million bolts a year, it is very important to use the smallest bolt that is strong enough. An extra penny on each bolt would cost the company an extra £10,000 a year.

Flat washer   Crinkle washer   Spring washer   Friction nut

Tapping

Tapping is the process of making a thread in a material for a bolt to screw into. A special tool called a tap is used to cut the thread. When a hole has been tapped, there is no need for a nut, as the bolt screws straight into the material and is held there by the thread.

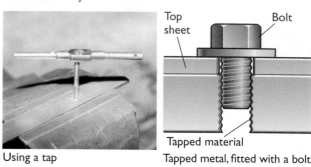

Using a tap

Tapped metal, fitted with a bolt

Self-tapping screws

Thin sheet metal and plastic can be fixed using self-tapping screws. As the screw is turned, it cuts its own thread in the material. This is a very quick way of making a joint.

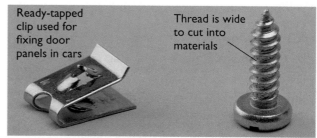

A ready-tapped clip and self-tapping screw

Using self-tapping screws

Plastic cases for electrical equipment are held together using self-tapping screws. For project work in school self-tapping screws are a quick and easy way of joining plastic parts.

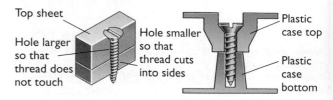

Wood

Screws and nails are the main temporary fixings for wood.

Wood screws

Wood screws have three parts: the head, the shank and the thread.

The head of a wood screw can be many shapes but the basic method of using a screw stays the same. Holes have to be made for the thread and the shank and sometimes the head as well.

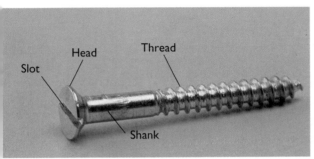
A woodscrew

Steps to fitting a wood screw

1 When the position of the screw has been marked, hold the two pieces of wood together and drill the **pilot hole**. This should be slightly shorter than the screw. The pilot hole is slightly thinner than the thread part of the screw, so that the thread will grip the sides of the wood.

2 Drill the **clearance hole** deep enough for the shank to fit into. The clearance hole is slightly wider than the thickness of the shank.

3 If the screw has a countersunk head, a countersink hole is used to allow the head of the screw to fit flush with the surface of the wood.

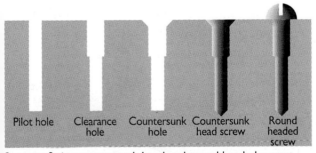

Pilot hole · Clearance hole · Countersunk hole · Countersunk head screw · Round headed screw

Steps to fitting countersunk head and round headed screws

Screw and drill sizes

The size of a screw is in two parts. The length of the screw is in inches and the thickness of the screw is a number. So you might buy a steel countersunk 1¼" No. 8.

A box of screws

In a DIY store, screws usually come in packs with this information on the front. The size of the screw depends on how it is to be used. Larger screws can withstand greater force.

The table below shows what size drill to use when fitting a wood screw. When screwing medium and thin screws into softwood, a bradawl is usually good enough to make the pilot hole.

Screw size	Pilot hole drill	Clearance hole drill
No. 4	1.5mm	3.0mm
No. 6	2.0mm	4.0mm
No. 8	2.5mm	4.5mm
No.10	2.5mm	5.0mm

Nails

Nails are often used to join wood permanently, but they can easily be pulled out if you need to take a wooden frame apart again.

Questions

1 What would happen if the pilot hole for a wood screw was too big?

2 What would be the advantage to a manufacturer of using self-tapping screws rather than wood screws?

3 Why are nuts and bolts usually used in metal joints, rather than screws?

Making the shape

Wood

Making a curved shape in wood can be difficult because the grain at the end tends to split. Always cut, plane and smooth *with* the grain, *not against* it. This helps to give a smooth and not a rough finish.

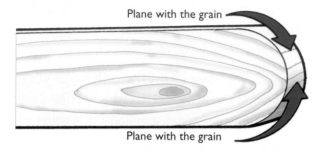

Thin sheet material like plywood and hardboard can be fixed to a frame to give a curved surface. The curve must not be too tight.

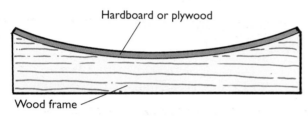

Thin strips of wood, called laminates, can be glued together and placed in a **former**. When the glue dries and the wood is removed from the former, it will stay in the bent shape.

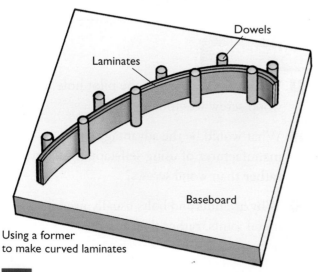

Using a former
to make curved laminates

Shaping edges

Objects made from wood can look clumpy and heavy if the edges are left square. A chamfer on the edge makes a wooden frame look far more attractive. Use a plane at 45 degrees to remove the sharp edge, gradually round the edge with the plane and finish with glasspaper.

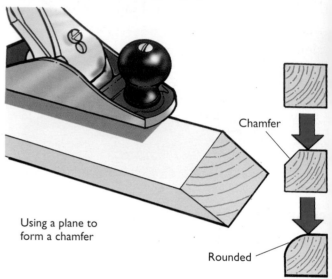

Using a plane to
form a chamfer

Shaping holes

1 Drill a 6mm hole on the waste wood side of the line.
2 Put a coping saw blade through the hole and fix it back on to the saw frame.
3 Saw just inside the line of the hole.
4 Finish with flat and rounded files.
5 Smooth with glasspaper.

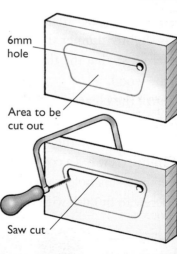

Stages in shaping a hole

Metal

Metal is ductile which means that it will bend without breaking.

To bend a steel bar you need to heat it up to make it softer. It is possible to use a hammer and cold bend steel, but it tends to crack and it is difficult to get good tight curves. Red hot steel can easily be bent with very little force. The correct safety equipment must be worn for this type of activity.

Making a curve on the outside of steel or aluminium is quite easy, but requires some effort:

1 Make one or more straight cuts to remove most of the metal outside the curve line.
2 File the remaining metal down to the curve line.

To get a good smooth curve, start with the end of the file on the part of the curve furthest from you and as you push forward, rock the file backwards and downwards.

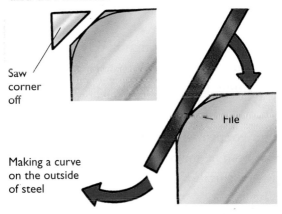

Saw corner off

File

Making a curve on the outside of steel

Casting and pressing materials

Metal, plastic and other materials can be cast into moulds. There are many dangers in casting metals, as high temperatures are needed. Casting has two main advantages over other ways of shaping metal:

1 There is very little waste produced.
2 The shape produced is the same each time.

Metal can be pressed into shapes which produce accurate parts economically. Car body panels are made in this way.

Plastic

Plastic sheet can be bent using a hot wire or hot element bender. Care must be taken not to burn yourself. Using protective gloves, hold the plastic over the hot part of the heat bender. When the plastic starts to move, take it away from the heat and bend it against a clean flat surface. The plastic needs to be held in place until it has cooled a little.

Strip heater for bending plastics

Hint

1 Do not leave plastic on the heat bender too long or it will start to bubble.
2 Plastic tends to 'recover' its shape a little after it is bent. You may need to bend it a little further than you think to end up with the right bend.
3 The thinner the wood laminate, the tighter the bend that can be made.

Questions

1 Why is casting a more economical way of producing shapes than cutting and shaping?

2 If only a few items are needed, they are made by hand rather than moulded. Explain why this is.

3 Why is it better to 'hot' bend steel rather than 'cold' bend it?

very useful materials because they ha... ery large range of properties and are easily formed into complicated shapes.

There are four main types of plastic moulding:

- blow moulding
- injection moulding
- vacuum forming
- extrusion.

All of these methods use a mould to give shape to the plastic. As the mould can be used many times, the same shape can be made over and over again, very accurately and cheaply.

Blow moulding

Air is blown into a hot hollow piece of plastic which has been placed inside a mould. The plastic blows up like a balloon and takes the shape of the inside of the mould. Where parts of the mould join, a ridge is left.

This manufacturing process is very quick and cheap but the cost of the machinery in the first place is quite high. Plastic milk containers are made in this way. Blow moulding does not produce strong items or ones with complicated shapes.

Blow moulding plastic

Blow moulded milk container

Injection moulding

With this method heated plastic is forced into a mould. The plastic fills gaps between parts of the mould.

Very complicated shapes can be moulded in this way and the accuracy of the items produced is excellent. Plastic bottle tops, spoons and the cases of pens are made like this. A large number of small items can be made at one time using this method.

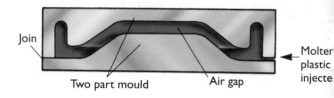

Plastic being injection moulded

Vacuum forming

This is a very cheap and common way of making plastic containers and trays. Most schools have a vacuum-forming machine and it is easy and fairly safe to use.

Making a vacuum-forming mould

The mould can be made out of almost anything. Wood is very suitable.

Whatever the shape you intend to mould, it must have an angle on the sides. If the sides of the mould are parallel, the plastic will grip the mould and you will not be able to remove it afterwards.

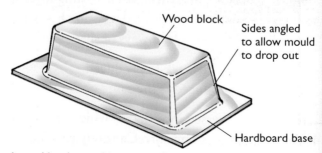

A mould to be used in vacuum-forming

1 When the mould is ready, place it in the vacuum forming machine. A heater like an electric grill will heat and soften a sheet of plastic.

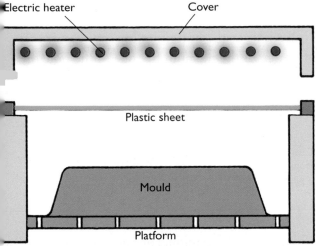

2 When the plastic is floppy, the mould is pushed up into the plastic, and the vacuum is turned on.

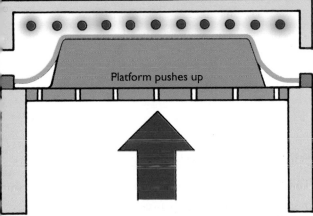

3 As the air is removed, the plastic sheet will fit over the mould.

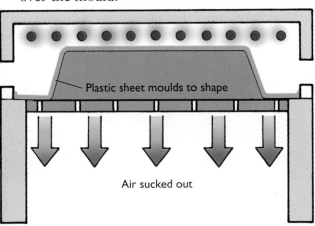

4 When the plastic has cooled a little, the mould can be removed and used again.

Common faults in vacuum forming

Webbing – this is a thin sheet of plastic which forms between two parts of a mould like the skin between the toes of a duck. Moulds that are too deep can web. This sometimes happens because the plastic was too hot before moulding.

An example of webbing

Holes – deep moulds can cause the plastic to become too thin making a hole. Once a hole has been made, air will get in and the plastic will not mould any more.

Plastic does not fit shape – if the plastic is not warm enough, it may not flow into the corners of the mould.

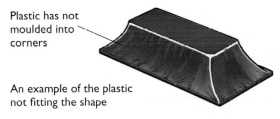

An example of the plastic not fitting the shape

Extrusion

With extrusion, plastic is forced through a shaped hole and comes out with the same **cross-section** as the hole. This method is used in double glazing, curtain rails, etc.

An extruded UPVC window sill

To do

Use clay or soft wood to make a mould of a letter of the alphabet. Your teacher will tell you what size, style and thickness to use. When you have completed the letter, explain your work in detail, using drawings and writing to say how you have achieved the shape.

Cutting and shaping metals

Metals are the hardest of the resistant materials, so specially hardened tools are needed to cut them.

Cutting metal

Metal shears used to cut thin sheet metal

For small strips of sheet metal or curves, use a pair of metal shears. These are very similar to scissors.

To cut larger sheets of metal in straight lines use a guillotine.

To cut metal bars or rods use either a junior hacksaw or a hacksaw, depending on the thickness of the material.

Using a hacksaw

Larger bars of metal should be cut using a mechanical saw.

To cut a slot from the edge of a piece of metal, drill a hole at the bottom of the slot. Cut from the edge of the metal to the side of the hole on either side. Finish the bottom of the slot using a square or flat file.

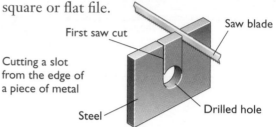

First saw cut

Saw blade

Cutting a slot from the edge of a piece of metal

Steel

Drilled hole

To cut a slot in the middle of a piece of metal, drill a series of holes along the slot and use an abrofile to cut from one hole to the next. Finish with a flat file.

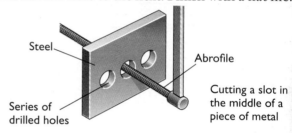

Steel

Abrofile

Series of drilled holes

Cutting a slot in the middle of a piece of metal

Bending metal

To bend a small thin piece of metal, grip it firmly in a vice and bend it with your hand. For slightly thicker pieces of metal use a hammer. For thicker strips of metal, heat the metal to a dull red and bend it in a former. For large sheets of metal, use a bending machine. This will give a much neater and sharper bend than doing it by hand.

Bending red hot steel

Letters can be punched into the surface of metal using a set of letter punches. *Try making a small nameplate with your initials.*

Making complicated shapes by cutting and bending metal is slow and expensive. It is also difficult to repeat the shapes accurately. To produce a number of items that are identical, a mould is needed.

Casting

Steel, aluminium and other metals can be heated so that they turn into a liquid. When metal becomes liquid it is called molten. Like any liquid, molten metal will take the shape of the container that it is in.

The two main methods of casting are called 'sand casting' and 'die casting'.

Sand casting – this method can be used for steel or aluminium. A mould is made and pushed into a box of sand. When the mould is removed, an impression is left in the sand. Molten metal is then poured into the impression and allowed to cool.

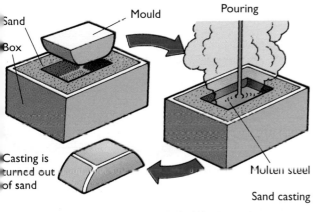

Sand casting

Die casting – suitable for aluminium as it has a much lower melting point than steel and so can be cast in a steel mould or die. The advantage of using a die is that the surface of the casting is much smoother than when cast in sand and the process is quicker.

Die cast metal toy van

Forging

If steel is heated so that it becomes soft it can be forced into a mould, called a die, using a very large force.

Drop forging is a common way of forming metal objects quickly. A large mass with a die on the underside is dropped on to a piece of hot metal sitting in another die. The soft metal is forced into the shape of the two dies. This is very fast compared to most other methods of production, but only simple shapes can be formed.

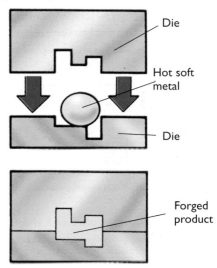

Forging a metal object

Pressing

Pressing is a very fast way of producing shaped sheet metal products which does not need heat. Most car body panels are made this way. Two matching dies are forced together to press the sheet into the required shape.

Questions

1 Why is it possible to die cast aluminium?

2 What are the main benefits of casting rather than bending and cutting steel?

3 Why is steel heated during drop forging?

4 Why is sand used in casting steel?

Cutting and shaping plastics

There are many different types of plastic, and some of the processes here are not suitable for all of them. Acrylic is probably the most common type of plastic you will meet. It can be cut and shaped like a very soft metal. The main problem with acrylic is that it tends to crack.

Getting the order right

It is important that you do things in the right order.

Cut material to size leaving enough spare material at the edge for smoothing

↓

Mark out shapes to be cut and lines for bending

↓

Drill all holes. It is easier to hold a rectangle when drilling than some other shape

↓

Cut internal holes and shapes

↓

Cut external shapes and curves

↓

File and finish internal holes

↓

File and finish external edges

↓

Bend using heat bender

↓

Remove protective covering

Process for making an acrylic letter rack

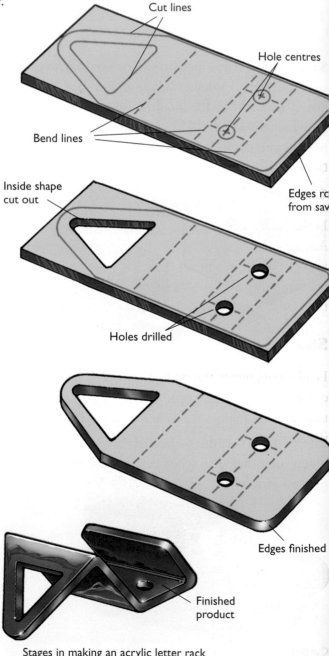

Cut lines

Hole centres

Bend lines

Edges ro
from saw

Inside shape
cut out

Holes drilled

Edges finished

Finished
product

Stages in making an acrylic letter rack

Drilling holes

Acrylic is a fairly soft material which cuts easily. If you use a normal twist drill bit, the plastic may catch on the cutting edge and climb up the drill bit. If this happens the plastic will often crack. Use a flat ended drill bit. This will scrape the plastic rather than cut it. The hole drills more slowly and the finish you get is much better. Always drill through the acrylic into a flat piece of wood. This stops the drill cracking the edge of the hole as it breaks through.

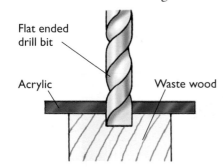

Drilling a piece of acrylic

Outside shapes

Hold the acrylic firmly using plastic vice jaws. Always hold the acrylic close to the cut you are making. This stops the saw from bending and cracking the material. You will need to keep moving the work in the vice to keep the cut supported.

Shaped holes

Drill a hole inside the waste material. Thread a coping saw blade through the hole and attach it to a coping saw frame. Saw carefully, staying just inside the line you have marked.

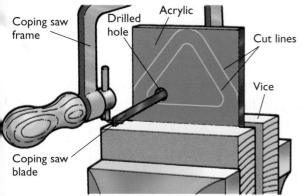

Cutting a hole in a piece of acrylic

When you have cut the waste section out, file the inside edge using a fine file with small teeth. Finish the edge using a scraper and metal polish.

Hint

If you have a straight edge to file, clamp a straight piece of wood along the edge and use this as a guide for your file.

Bending

Bending the material is usually the last thing you do before the project is finished. This is because it is difficult to hold the work when it is bent.

Place the bend line over the hot part of the heater and wait until it starts to sag down. Remove the plastic from the heat and hold it against a clean flat surface to bend it into shape. Do not try to hurry the cooling using cold water. When the plastic has cooled, the bend will stay.

If you leave the plastic on the heater for too long, the surface will bubble and the plastic will change colour.

Bent plastic bulges slightly at the edges. If two edges are to be bent next to each other, a slight hollow must be made to allow space for the bulges.

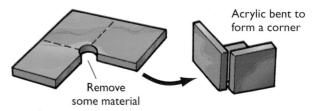

Bending a piece of acrylic

To do

Make a simple key fob using plastic. You will need to drill a small hole towards one edge of the fob before you start to cut out the shape. Spend a few minutes planning the shape before you start – keep it simple. Avoid sharp corners and thin sections.

Setting up a plane

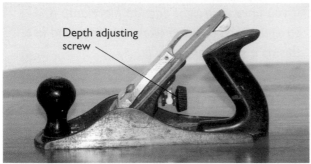

A smoothing plane

The depth adjusting screw needs to be turned so that the blade is only just visible when you look along the sole of the plane. The shavings you get should be thin.

Plane away from the grain to get a good finish. If the wood seems to rough up, try planing in the other direction.

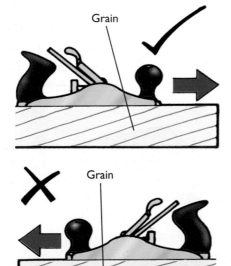

The aim of planing is to get a flat square surface. To test for flatness, hold a steel rule against the surface. If there are any hollows these will show up as places where light gets through. The high points will be where the light does not get through. Mark the high spots with a pencil and plane these off.

To test for squareness, use a try square. Hold the square to the edge and see if there are any gaps. Slide the try square along the wood to see if it is square all the way along.

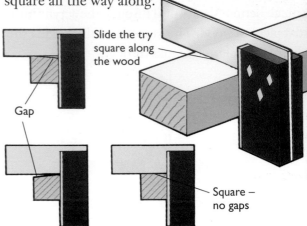

Using a try square to test for squareness

Planing a chamfer

To improve the look of a wooden design, the edge can be chamfered by planing the edge at an angle. To cut a chamfer, hold a plane at 45 degrees to the surface and plane the edge.

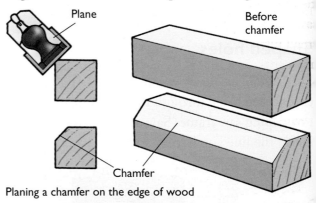

Planing a chamfer on the edge of wood

A curve can be put on the edge of the wood in a similar way by planing at different angles and then sanding the edge.

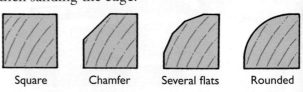

Stages in putting a curve on the edge of wood

Planing across the end grain is very difficult. You need a very sharp plane. Clamp a piece of waste wood to the edge of the work to stop the edge from splitting.

Preparing to plane across the end grain

To curve the end of a piece of wood, use a coping saw. Make sure that you hold the saw at right angles to the wood or the cut surface will slope. Finish off by planing with the grain. If you need two matching curves, cut and plane both pieces of wood at the same time. They can be held together with double-sided tape.

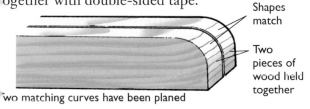
Two matching curves have been planed

Cutting a joint

Hold the wood firmly using a bench hook or a vice. Saw on the waste wood side of the line, keeping the saw vertical. The more accurate the saw cut, the better the joint will fit. To remove small bits of wood which are left in the corner, use a sharp chisel to cut across the grain and remove the unwanted wood.

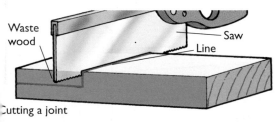
Cutting a joint

To remove a section of wood

Saw down either side of the section and then clamp the wood in a vice.

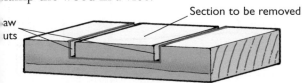

Use a chisel to remove small layers of wood at the corners. Work upwards from both sides to create a 'ridge' in the middle.

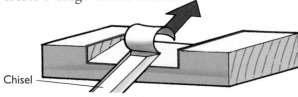

Then chisel across the top of the ridge to remove the rest of the wood.

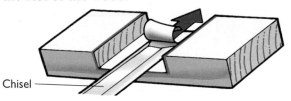

To remove a 'finger' of wood at the end of the grain, place the wood flat onto a piece of waste wood. Use a chisel which is the same size or slightly smaller than the finger you want to remove. Place the chisel blade with the bevel away from the cut line, about 1mm from the line. When the chisel cuts into the wood it tends to move away from the bevel side a little.

Use a mallet to cut through the grain. Work from both sides, turning the wood over frequently. To remove wide fingers, make several cuts into the finger and remove one at a time.

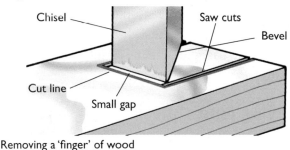
Removing a 'finger' of wood

To do

Make a display showing the correct way to saw to a marked line. Include examples of correct and incorrect cuts. These should include sawing the wrong side of the line, sawing too far from the line and sawing at an angle. Use drawings to highlight the errors.

Wood joints

Butt joint

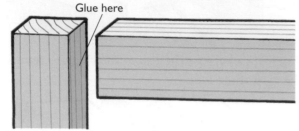

Glue here

This is the simplest type of joint. One piece of wood is pushed or butted against another. All that is needed is a flat square end on one piece of wood.

Butt joints are very weak, so they are only used where strength is not important.

Jinks joint

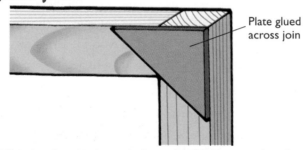

Plate glued across join

This is a butt joint reinforced with a triangle of card or wood. The extra strength comes from the increased area that is glued. It doesn't look very nice and the triangle of material juts out behind the joint.

Halving joint

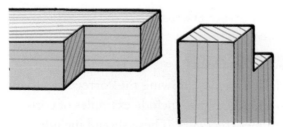

The halving joint is a fairly easy and quick joint to make, and it is quite strong. The visible end grain makes the joint less attractive than some more complicated joints.

'T' halving joint

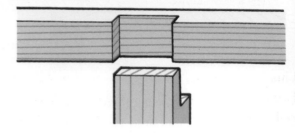

The 'T' halving joint shown here is very similar to the halving joint, but one piece of wood joins another in the middle. It is a little more difficult to make than the ordinary halving joint.

Cross halving joint

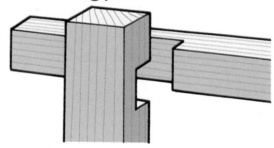

A cross halving joint is very strong but it takes practice to make it fit well.

The three types of halving joint can be put together to give attractive shapes. They are put together when a strong frame is necessary. An example is shown below.

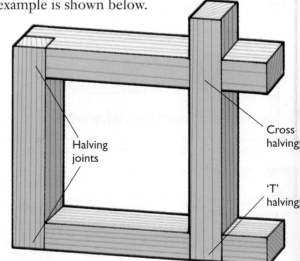

Halving joints

Cross halving

'T' halving

Dowel joint

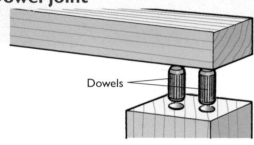

Dowels

This is a quick and accurate way of joining wood. Two dowels fit into holes in the wood. The only tool that is needed is a drill. A doweling jig can be used to help make sure that the holes are drilled in the right places. Dowel joints are very strong and cheap to make. This type of joint is often used in the manufacture of furniture.

Lap joint

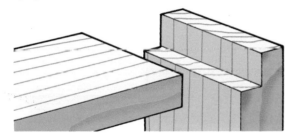

Lap joints are used to join boards at corners. It is an easy and attractive joint and it is quite strong.

Hint

To help cut the lap joint, clamp a scrap piece of wood to the work as a guide.

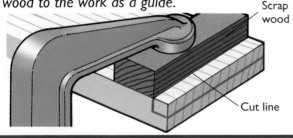

Scrap wood

Cut line

To do

Make one of the joints shown here and then explain the steps needed to make it.

Housing joint

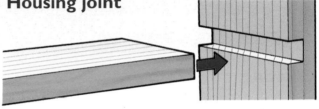

A housing joint is used for shelves and partitions, and gives an attractive finish. This joint is very strong and quite easy to make.

Fillets

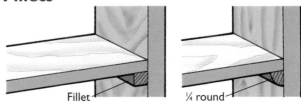

Fillet   ¼ round

To strengthen a joint, a small section of wood called a fillet can be glued into the corner. This increases the glued area and also supports the joint. The disadvantage is that it spoils the look of the design. Use quarter round wood to make the fillet look more attractive.

Finger joint

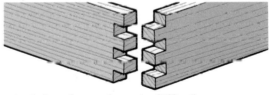

The finger joint shown here is difficult to cut well using hand tools, but it is attractive and very strong. It is used a lot in the furniture industry. Special tools make it quick and accurate to make.

Dovetail joint

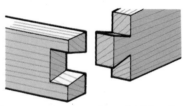

This is the strongest and probably the most attractive joint used in wood, but it is also very hard to make accurately. Dovetails are used in high quality furniture to attach drawer fronts.

Metal joints

Riveting

Rivets are a quick and permanent way of joining metal sheets or fairly thin pieces of metal without expensive equipment. (See also page 48.)

How to rivet two pieces of metal

1 Mark, centre punch and drill two holes in one of the pieces of metal, using a 3.3mm drill bit.

2 Mark, centre punch and drill one hole in the other piece of metal.

3 Use a 3mm rivet to peg the pieces of metal together.

4 Mark through the second hole with a scriber. This will accurately show where the second hole should be drilled.

5 Centre punch and drill the second hole.

6 Countersink the top of the top piece of metal and the bottom of the bottom piece of metal.

7 Drill through the holes again with the 3.3mm drill bit. This will clear the **burr** of metal which the countersink has made. If not cleared away, the burr will stop the rivet going through.

8 Put both rivets through the holes from the back and lay the work on a metal block. The rivet heads should be on the metal block and the small ends of the rivets should be sticking up towards you. Use a hammer to flatten the ends of the rivets. This will make the rivet fill up the countersink.

9 Finally file off the parts of the rivet which are **proud** or sticking up, so that you cannot feel it.

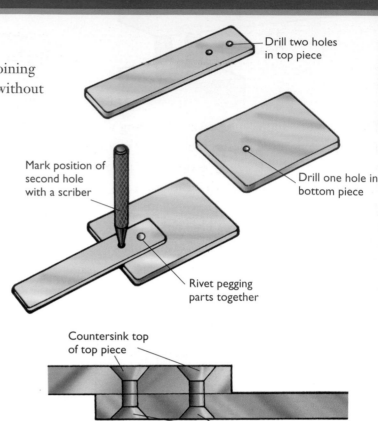

Drill two holes in top piece

Mark position of second hole with a scriber

Drill one hole in bottom piece

Rivet pegging parts together

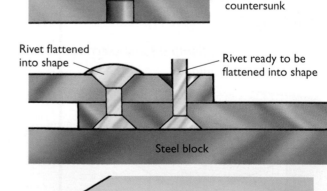

Countersink top of top piece

Countersink bottom of bottom piece

Burr formed when hole was countersunk

Rivet flattened into shape

Rivet ready to be flattened into shape

Steel block

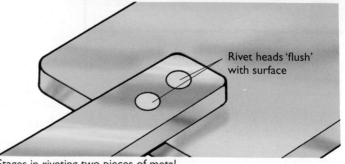

Rivet heads 'flush' with surface

Stages in riveting two pieces of metal

Brazing

This is a hazardous process and needs the correct tools, safety equipment and supervision.

Brazing is the bonding of two pieces of steel using a brazing rod. The brazing rod melts and flows between the two pieces of steel and joins them as it cools. To make the metal in the brazing rod flow, the steel must be very clean and coated with flux. If the steel is not clean or flux is not used, the joint will be very weak.

How to braze two pieces of metal

1 Clean the parts of the steel which need to be joined. Use a file and then emery cloth. The steel should be bright and shiny.
2 Place flux on to the steel.
3 Hold the steel to be joined in position, so that the surfaces touch.

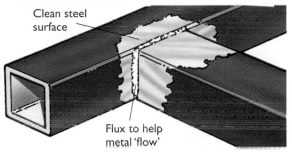

Clean steel surface

Flux to help metal 'flow'

4 Heat the join with a gas torch until the steel is red hot.
5 Gently place the brazing rod against the join.
6 The brazing rod will melt and flow between the pieces of steel.

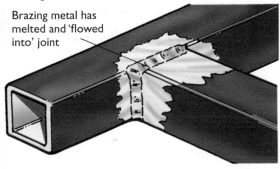

Brazing metal has melted and 'flowed into' joint

7 Allow the join to cool. Do not try to hurry the cooling with cold water.

Industrial joints

Most permanent steel joints used in industry are welded. Gas welding gives a very strong join but requires a lot of skill and is fairly slow. Electric welding is much faster and can be **automated**.

The car industry uses electric welding. The body panels of a car are often spot welded.

Spot welding a pipe

The spot welding process can be done using robots.

Robot welding in the car industry

Questions

1 Why is flux used in the brazing process?

2 Why is it best to do all the shaping and filing before riveting two pieces of metal together?

3 On a bicycle the frame is welded together but other parts are bolted on. Explain why different methods of joining are used on a bicycle.

Fixings and fittings

Nails

Nails for fixing wood come in different shapes and sizes, depending on the job they have to do. All nails work in the same way. Friction between the sides of the nail and the wood holds the pieces of wood together.

Panel pins are small thin nails which can hold thin sheet material on to a frame. They are used to hold pieces of wood together while glue sets.

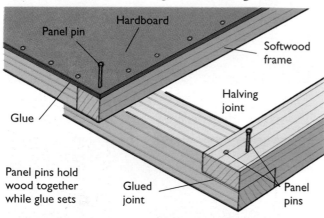

Panel pins hold wood together while glue sets

For thicker wood, clamps are used to hold parts together while the glue sets.

Although nails are quite a quick way of fixing wood, sometimes they are not quick enough. Fence panels, frames and other wood products which need to be made cheaply are stapled using a staple gun. Ten staples can be fired from a gun in the time it takes to put in one or two nails. The staple gun also needs less effort.

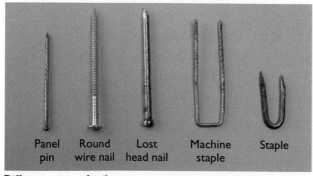

Different types of nail

Nails are very cheap to make and use, but they do not give a very strong join on their own.

Screws

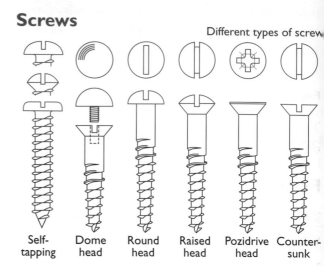

Different types of screw

Self-tapping, Dome head, Round head, Raised head, Pozidrive head, Counter-sunk

Wood screws

A countersunk head screw with a slotted screwdriver

Wood screws have a countersunk head so that the top of the screw lies flush with the surface of the wood. They have slotted heads for use with a slotted screwdriver.

Crosshead screws

A crosshead screw with a crosshead screwdriver

Philips and pozidrive screws have a star-shaped slot for the screwdriver.

This type of screw head is useful for fast fixing using an electric screwdriver. It is easier to keep the screwdriver in the head of the screw. For manufacturing, this type of screw cuts down on labour time.

Round-headed screws

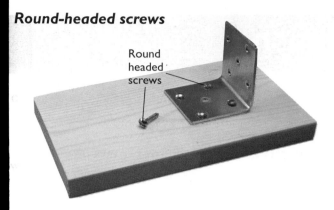

Round headed screws

Fixing a metal bracket to a piece of wood

These screws are used to hold some metal parts on to wood or brick walls.

Furniture

The metal parts fixed to doors and other wooden structures are called furniture.

Hinges – the cheapest type of hinge is a butt hinge. These can be made out of steel or brass. They are strong and fairly easy to use.

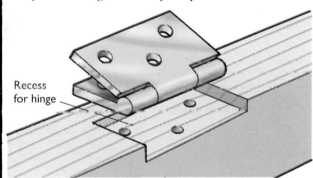

Recess for hinge

Fitting a hinge to a piece of wood

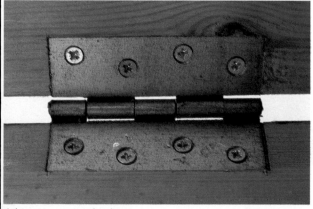

A hinge on a wooden box

Hasp and staple – a hasp and staple is a very easy and cheap way of attaching a lockable fixing to a door or lid.

Because the hasp and staple is on the outside of a door it is not very secure.

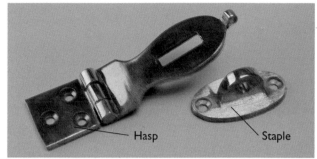

Hasp   Staple

A hasp and staple

Locks – there are many types of lock available. Some can be mounted on the surface of wood, but the better ones are recessed into the wood.

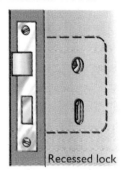

Surface mount lock   Recessed lock

Questions

1. Why is the head of a wood screw countersunk?

2. Why do nails give a weaker join than screws?

3. Why are pozidrive and Philips screw heads used in the manufacturing industry, rather than wood screws?

4. Why are nails cheaper to make than screws?

To do

Make a display showing a range of nails and screws and their uses.

Getting a smooth finish

Preparing a surface for paint or varnish is very important.

Making it smooth

A surface may look smooth but it is actually covered with tiny scratches.

An **abrasive** is used to produce a smooth surface.

Wood surfaces

Glasspaper is a strong sheet of paper with particles of glass stuck to it. The sharp corners of the glass scratch a thin layer of wood off the surface.

Coarse glasspaper has large particles of glass. It removes layers of wood quickly, but it also leaves deep scratches. Fine glasspaper has small particles of glass. It leaves only small scratches, but it removes layers of wood more slowly. Flour paper is a very fine grade of glasspaper used to produce an extra smooth finish.

Unfinished wood surface
↓
Coarse glasspaper removes marks on wood
↓
Medium glasspaper removes large scratches left by coarse glasspaper
↓
Fine glasspaper removes scratches left by medium glasspaper
↓
Smooth wood surface

The process for sanding wood

Glasspaper should always be used along the grain. If you sand across the grain you will leave marks.

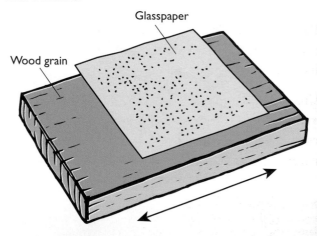

Use the glasspaper along the grain of wood

Different grades of glasspaper

Hint

Sand before gluing. This avoids having to sand into difficult corners.

68

Metal and plastic

When plastic or metal are cut, deep scratches are left from the teeth of the saw. You will need to remove these scratches with a file. File along the edge, not across it. Filing the wrong way can leave an uneven edge and can cause plastic to crack.

Plastic surfaces

Plastic usually comes protected by a thin film. The film should be left on as long as possible to protect the highly polished surface.

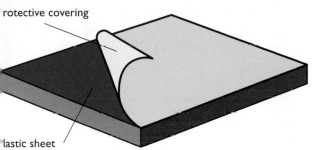

Plastic protected by a thin film

protective covering

plastic sheet

Always use a file with fine teeth on plastic. A coarse file will leave deep scratches and is more likely to crack your work.

After filing, scrape the edge of the plastic with a craft knife. This will remove a very fine layer and leave a smooth finish. To get a mirror finish use metal polish or a buffer.

Drag a craft knife blade at an angle along the edge of the plastic using light pressure

Metal surfaces

To remove deep scratches from metal you must use a medium or coarse file. To make the metal smoother, use a file with fine teeth.

For very smooth finishes you should use a piece of **emery cloth**. This comes in different grades. A fine grade emery cloth will leave a very smooth surface.

For a mirror finish on metal you must use metal polish or a buffer.

Smoothing with power

Your school may have either a belt sander or a disc sander. These are very useful, but care should be taken when using them.

Remember the quality of the finished object is only as good as the quality of the finished surface.

Questions

1 Should you sand wood along the grain or across the grain? What happens if you do it the wrong way?

2 What is meant by the word 'grade' when talking about glasspaper or emery cloth?

3 Why are different grades of glasspaper used?

4 What might happen if you file across the edge of a piece of plastic and not along it?

5 Why has metal polish got very small hard particles in it?

6 Commercially made furniture is designed to need the minimum of sanding. Why is this?

Strength by design

Anything you make will need to be able to keep its shape and have some strength.

Strength comes from three things:

1 The material (cardboard, steel, etc.)
2 The shape (how it is put together)
3 The cross-section (the shape inside).

The material

This will have the greatest effect on strength, but the need for strength must be balanced by cost and other factors. Below is a table showing the strength of some common materials.

Material	Force needed to break a 1mm square piece of material
Steel	400 Newtons
Aluminium	160 Newtons
Hardwood	150 Newtons
Softwood	100 Newtons
String	50 Newtons
Cardboard	30 Newtons

Composite materials

Sometimes the properties of two materials are needed to do a job. A composite is something made up of two or more materials, for example, electric power cables, which are made up of aluminium with steel for strength, or prestressed concrete beams which are strengthened with steel rods.

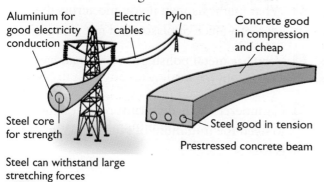

Aluminium for good electricity conduction

Electric cables   Pylon

Steel core for strength

Steel can withstand large stretching forces

Concrete good in compression and cheap

Steel good in tension

Prestressed concrete beam

The new materials

Modern science has given us many new materials such as plastic and complicated metal alloys. One of the new materials which gives exceptional strength with very low weight is carbon fibre. It is now possible to make very light bicycles and extra long fishing rods using carbon fibre.

Carbon fibre rods are light and strong

The shape

Shape is very important when designing for strength. Triangles are usually the strongest shape but sometimes other factors will mean that other shapes must be used.

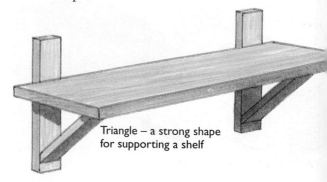

Triangle – a strong shape for supporting a shelf

The cross-section

This is the shape you see if you cut across the material. A piece of material can be made much stiffer by changing the cross section.

Cross-sections of plastic beams

All three of these plastic beams use the same amount of material, but the shapes are different. The solid cross-section on the left is easy to bend. The other two cross-section shapes are much stiffer but still use the same amount of material.

There are many good reasons why hollow beams are used instead of solid ones.

Cost – they need less material, which lowers the cost.

Weight – designing structures to be strong using less material reduces weight. All types of transport use this idea to save fuel.

Appearance – structures are more graceful if they have a 'good' shape.

Plastics are modern materials and, because they can be easily moulded, are often formed with hollows to reduce cost and increase strength. Webbing is used to give stiffness and strength while needing the minimum of material.

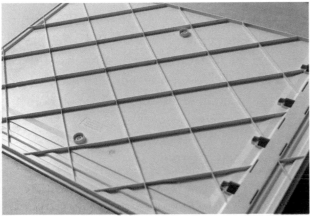

Webbing gives stiffness to plastic

Nature has developed the use of hollow materials. Most birds have bones which are hollow. This reduces their weight and makes it easier for them to fly.

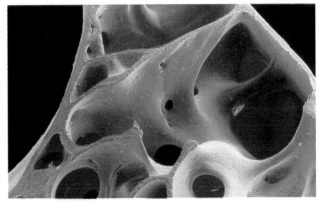

Internal structure of a bird bone

To do

Make paper tubes in different shapes, using the same amount of paper for each, and test their bending strength.

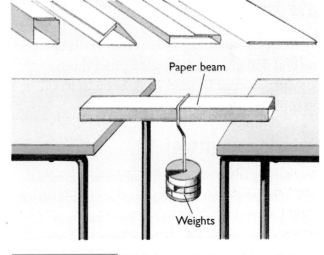

Paper beam

Weights

Questions

1 Why are the metal legs of school chairs hollow?

2 Some cars are made with aluminium body panels but a steel frame underneath. Why?

3 Why are hollow aluminium beams used for making aircraft?

Decorative finishes

Washes

Green wash Brush

Natural wood colour

Putting a wash on a piece of wood

Thinned water-based paint can be painted on to wood. This is called a wash and gives colour to the wood but still shows the grain. A wash makes a good background for further painting or can be left as it is.

Acrylic paints

These are wonderful paints as they are easy to use and will give a bright waterproof finish. Acrylic paint can be used straight on to wood, or on top of varnish.

Painting on metal

Best results when painting metal are achieved if a special type of paint called primer is painted on to the bare metal. It is best to use gloss paints or acrylic paints on metal as the water in water-based paints tends to make steel rust. The protection that gloss paints give steel is very important; without this protection, it will quickly rust, particularly if it is outside. Gloss paints can also be used on wood.

Flicking

Use water-based paint on a toothbrush and pull your thumb towards you. As the bristles spring back into place, the paint is flicked. This can give an attractive speckle to a surface.

Air-brush

Even beginners can get a good result with an air-brush. A stream of air picks up ink or paint and blows it on to a surface. Delicate shading can be achieved in this way and, with practice, some outstanding results are possible. The type of ink or paint used will change the type of finish you get. A very cheap version of an air-brush is available which can be used with felt pens, and this can transform the presentation of project work.

Sponging

Use a natural sponge, ordinary synthetic sponge or crushed newspaper. Dip it into paint and gently touch the surface. The random patterns produced are very attractive.

Sponge

Sponged paint

Natural wood

Sponging a piece of wood

Dipping

This is an excellent technique for getting a first class finish on metal surfaces. The metal is heated in an oven and then dipped into special plastic granules. The granules melt and flow over the surface of the metal which is then lifted out and allowed to cool. As soon as the metal has cooled, the plastic coating sets and produces a smooth waterproof surface.

Permanent pens

Permanent pens can be used to decorate plastic objects. Avoid large blocks of colour as the finish tends to be uneven.

Stencils

A stencil is an excellent way of producing the same shape several times. With practice the shape can be produced fairly accurately.

Making a stencil

A stencil can be made from almost anything, but the best material is clear plastic sheet. Cut the shape out of the sheet leaving enough blank sheet around it to protect the background from accidental marks.

Put the stencil over the background and hold it in place with masking tape. Carefully paint or spray the stencil.

Painted shape   Stencil

Masking

This is similar to stencilling, but the mask is not reusable. Stick two pieces of tape to the surface, leaving a gap. Paint the surface between the two pieces of tape and then remove them.

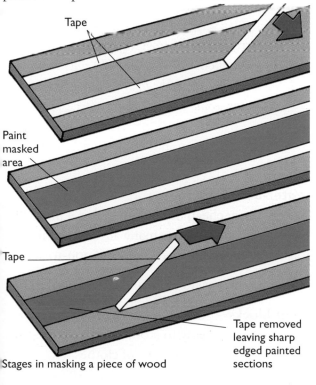

Tape

Paint masked area

Tape

Tape removed leaving sharp edged painted sections

Stages in masking a piece of wood

Wood stain

There are many wood stain colours available. Some colours make the surface a similar colour to another type of wood, and some are straight colours. It is best to varnish the wood after staining. This will stop the stain getting on to people's hands and clothes, as well as giving a glossy finish.

Coloured varnishes are also available, although it is not as easy to get a good finish with these.

Using coloured woods

One of the most dramatically beautiful effects is the use of different coloured woods to contrast with each other. This can be done in two ways. Solid woods can be glued to each other or thin sheets of wood called veneers can be glued to a surface. For complicated designs, veneers are used. This is called marquetry.

Marquetry using different coloured wood veneers

Chessboard using contrasting colours of solid wood

Pyrography

This is an ancient method of decorating wood. Patterns are burnt into the surface with a hot tool. For safety reasons an electric pyrography tool is best.

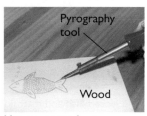

Pyrography tool

Wood

Using pyrography to apply design

To do

Make a series of stencils using cardboard. Choose a theme like animals or space. Use the stencils to decorate a sheet of paper.

Varnish and paint

Varnish

Varnish gives a clear finish which lets the beauty of wood show through. Varnish protects wood from the environment, particularly water. The surface finish you end up with depends on the type of varnish you use.

Types of varnish

Gloss – a shiny smooth surface.
Silk – a slightly dull shiny surface.
Matt – a dull surface.

Some varnish contains colour and can be used to make fairly cheap wood look like an expensive hardwood. Quick drying varnishes are useful, but do not use them on top of water-based paint. It makes the paint run.

High gloss finish and matt finish

What goes wrong with varnish?

If you put the varnish on too thickly, it will take a very long time to dry. It will also tend to run, forming lines and drops.

Remember, dust or scratches which are not removed before varnishing will show up, so it is very important to get a good surface first.

Using varnish

Step 1   Make sure that the wood surface is really smooth with no scratches. *Any scratches will show up more when varnish is applied.*

Step 2   Wipe the surface with a clean cloth and a little white spirit. *This will remove any dust.*

Step 3   Apply the first coat of varnish thinned with a little white spirit. *This will help the first coat to soak into the surface.*

Step 4   When the first coat is dry, use a fine glasspaper to rub the surface down lightly. *Some wood fibres will stick up as the first coat of varnish soaks in.*

Step 5   Put a second coat of varnish on and allow to dry. *This coat will not soak in because the first coat has sealed the wood surface.*

Step 6   Use a very fine glass paper to slightly roughen the surface and apply the final coat of varnish. *The slightly rough surface helps the final coat to hold on to the second coat.*

Paint

Water-based paint

This is a very cheap method of giving a finished colour to wood, and has many advantages: it is washable, cheap, quick drying, and non-toxic.

There are three ways of buying water-based paints:

Paint blocks – these are very useful as they are easy to store and the paint washes out of clothes.

Powder paint – can be messy, but colours are more easily mixed.

Ready mixed – easy to use and gives a good dense colour. A little more expensive than other ways of buying paint.

Because these paints can be washed out in water they are not suitable for outside use or even where people may put damp fingers on them. A coat of varnish can help here, making the surface water resistant.

Gloss paints

These are more expensive than water-based paints, but they are waterproof and give a nice glossy finish. The big disadvantage with gloss paints is that they are not washable, so clothes will be permanently stained. They also take a long time to dry.

Acrylic paints

These have all the advantages of gloss paints but can be removed from clothing if washed immediately. They are very quick drying and leave a good dense colour which is waterproof. The main disadvantage is their cost, which is higher than either water-based or gloss paint.

Painting tips

- Make sure that the brushes you are using are clean before you start.
- Make sure that the surface you are painting on to is dry before you start painting a second coat or another colour on top.
- Where several colours are to be used, put the light colours on first as the dark ones will be difficult to cover up.

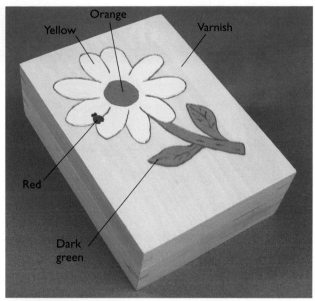

A painted wooden box

Which paint to use?

Paint type	Use
Gloss	Large or small areas of wood or metal, outside or inside
Acrylic	Small detail on wood or metal, inside or outside
Water-based	Large or small areas of wood or paper-based surfaces, inside

Cleaning up

Always wash brushes immediately after use. Gloss paint and varnish will need white spirit, and takes much longer to clean up than acrylic or water-based paints. Use newspaper under the objects to be painted to stop paint getting on to the benches.

To do

Paint a piece of wood with a selection of different coloured paints. When the paints have dried, varnish the wood. Are there any paints which look better after varnishing? Do some lose their colour? Write a brief account of the colours that look best after being varnished.

Case study in design part 1

This case study follows the designing and making of a simple object. It is an example of how a project could be carried out, and each section gives highlights of the various stages of the design process.

The problem

Jewellery left on a dressing table looks untidy and can easily get lost. The variety of items makes it difficult to keep them organized.

The problem!

Brief

Design and make a storage system for jewellery, to be used in a teenager's bedroom.

Key features

This is the result of a brainstorming activity. The most important aspects of the project are identified.

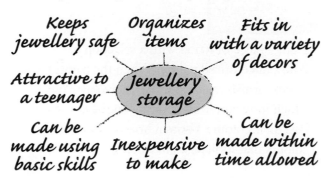

Specification

1 Materials cost less than £2.50.

2 Can be made within six weeks of lessons.

3 Uses materials and equipment which are available.

4 Neutral colour to fit in with a variety of bedroom decorations.

5 Attractive to people aged 11–14.

6 Holds a range of jewellery.

7 Keeps jewellery safe from accidental loss.

Research

Basic research has shown the following:

- jewellery includes earrings, necklaces, bangles, rings and brooches
- some form of multi-coloured geometric design will prove attractive to teenagers
- rings are a maximum of 25mm across, and bangles 80mm

Planning

This outlines the time the whole project will take.

Activity	Weeks					
	1	2	3	4	5	6
Brief and specification	■					
Research		■				
Ideas and development			■			
Final design				■		
Make and evaluate					■	■

A time chart for the project

Design ideas

Glass fronted
shelved cupboard

Partitioned box

Jewellery
tree

Set of
drawers

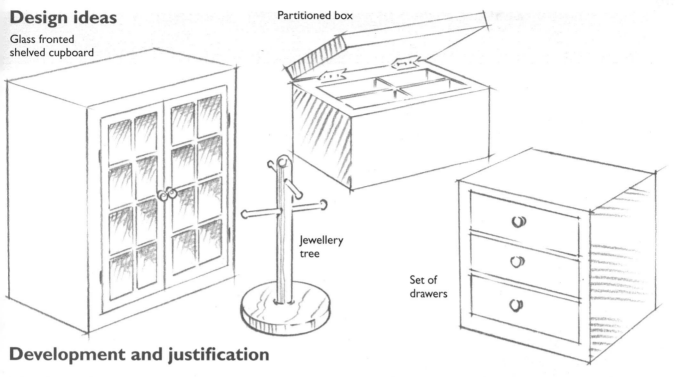

Development and justification

The chosen design is a development of the partitioned box. Softwood will be used for the box sides and lid as it is fairly cheap and blends in with most backgrounds.

Lap joints will be used for the box sides as they are reasonably strong but also straightforward to make.

Strips of wood will be glued to the inside of the box to form a ridge to support the plastic tray.

A clear plastic tray will be made for holding rings. This will be easy and quick to make and will increase the number of storage compartments in the box.

The box will have a hardboard base. It is cheap and easy to attach.

A padded lid to pin brooches to will be attached to the underside of the lid. The lid is hinged to display the brooches when open.

The final design idea

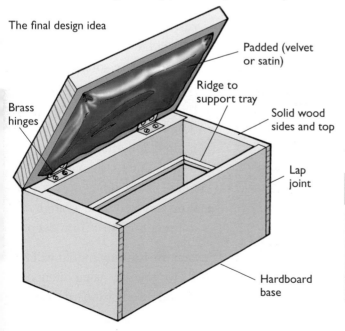

Padded (velvet or satin)

Ridge to support tray

Brass hinges

Solid wood sides and top

Lap joint

Hardboard base

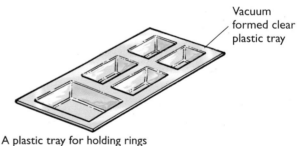

Vacuum formed clear plastic tray

A plastic tray for holding rings

To do

Sketch an alternative design based on one of the design ideas. Try to add features to make the design more useful. Explain why each part of your design has been chosen.

Final design

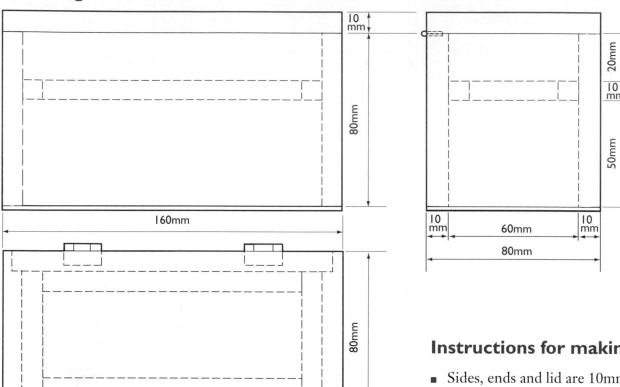

Parts list

Part name	Material	Length	Width	Thickness	Qty
Lid	Softwood	160	80	10	1
Side	Softwood	150	80	10	2
End	Softwood	80	80	10	2
Base	Hardboard	160	80	3	1
Side ridge	Softwood	120	10	10	2
End ridge	Softwood	60	10	10	2
Cushion	Satin	170	90		1
Padding	Wadding	150	70		1
Hinges	Brass				2

Note: all measurements in mm

Instructions for making

- Sides, ends and lid are 10mm thick softwood.
- Lid will be attached to box by brass hinges.
- The tray will be vacuum formed and fit inside box, resting on ridge.
- The ridge will be made from 10mm square softwood.
- The base will be hardboard, pinned and glued to the box.
- The box will be lap jointed, pinned and glued.
- The padded satin will be glued to the lid.
- The tray will have a range of depressions, all 15mm deep.

A vacuum-forming mould will be made for the tray using offcuts of softwood on a hardboard base.

Flow chart for making

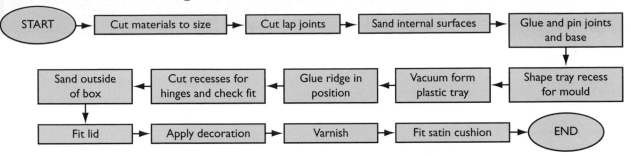

START → Cut materials to size → Cut lap joints → Sand internal surfaces → Glue and pin joints and base → Shape tray recess for mould → Vacuum form plastic tray → Glue ridge in position → Cut recesses for hinges and check fit → Sand outside of box → Fit lid → Apply decoration → Varnish → Fit satin cushion → END

The finished item

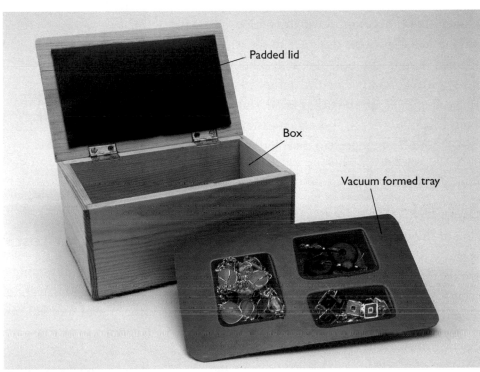

Padded lid

Box

Vacuum formed tray

The finished product

Evaluation

The following parts of the project could have been improved. Joints – there are some gaps where the joints are fitted. These are due to poor sawing finish. The gaps have been filled. Future projects will need greater accuracy of sawing. The lid does not lie flat when closed. This is due to the warping of the lid. Although the vacuum-formed tray fits well, it is difficult to lift out. Future designs will need to incorporate some form of finger grip.

The surface designs worked well and the general appearance is good. The choice of gloss varnish was correct as it gives the box an attractive finish.

To do

Draw a full size set of plans for the jewellery box from the information on this page.

Models

What is a model?

A model can be a smaller scale version of a design, or it can be full scale but made out of different materials.

Why make a model?

Modelling is important for many reasons. A small scale model allows the designer to see what the finished design will look like. It also helps the designer to communicate the design to others. A full scale model, on the other hand, can help with the designing process. It is much easier to try things out on a model than on the real thing.

How to model

Computer

One of the most important tools that designers now use is the computer. A computer model or simulation is a very fast and cheap way to see what a design would look like. It is very easy to change shapes and colours in seconds.

Cardboard

Cardboard is good for modelling shapes and mechanisms very quickly.

Cardboard model for a coin collecting box

Kits

Technical modelling kits like Lego and Fischer Technic can let you model complicated gear and lever systems quickly. These are particularly useful when designing systems to be controlled by computer.

Computer control of mechanism

Models for testing

A company designing a new product often uses a scale model for testing. This makes it much cheaper to find out how the product will behave than if a **prototype** was built.

Prototypes

A prototype is a full scale object made in the same materials, and in the same way, as the real production version would be. Prototypes are very expensive but they can save many millions of pounds by showing faults in the design before the product goes into production.

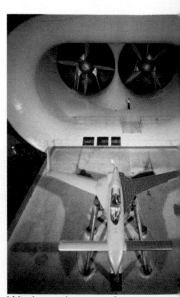

Wind tunnel testing of experimental aircraft

Techniques for modelling

Curved shapes

These can be made using chicken wire, papier-mâché and filler. Although with this method a model takes a long time to make, the results can be excellent. Surface detail can be added to represent grass or gravel by gluing coloured plastic granules to the finished shape.

Model golf course

Stiffening

Cardboard tends to bend, which can spoil a model. To make it stiffer, glue a strip of cardboard to the surface. For wide surfaces, use cross strips as well.

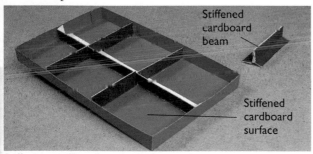

Stiffened cardboard beam

Stiffened cardboard surface

Stiffening cardboard

Movement

Paper fasteners can be used as pivots for joints in cardboard and plastic. Two paper fasteners can give a non-moving joint.

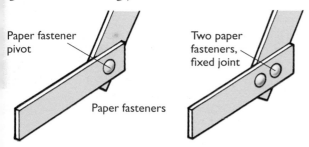

Paper fastener pivot

Two paper fasteners, fixed joint

Paper fasteners

Model of a stamping machine

For working models which are going to move in a realistic way, either use construction kits or easily worked resistant materials.

Scale

It is best to choose a scale which is easy to work out: 1:2, 1:5 or 1:10. Make sure that the important detail you need to show will not be lost by a very small scale model. It can be useful to choose a scale which is the same as existing models, e.g. people or cars.

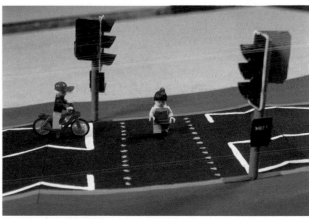

Model of a pelican crossing using the same scale as lego people

To do

1 Make a 1:20 scale model of your bedroom, without furniture.

2 Design and make your own furniture, carpets, wallpaper, etc.

Electricity

It is useful for you to have an understanding of how electric circuits work. Simple circuits can easily be built into resistant material project work.

Current flow

For electricity to flow there must be a complete circuit, from positive to negative. If the circuit is broken anywhere, then the electricity will not flow.

Materials that let electricity flow easily are called conductors. Materials that stop electricity flowing are called insulators.

The flow of electricity is called electric current. A bright bulb will have more electric current flowing through it than a dim bulb.

Resistors

Resistors are **components** which limit the flow of electric current. How much the flow is limited is measured in **ohms**. Resistors are usually quite small components with coloured bands. The first three coloured bands show the resistor value (see below). The fourth colour band shows the tolerance of the resistor value, e.g. gold is 5 per cent, silver is 10 per cent.

Resistor colour code

Resistors have four colour bands on them. The first colour band shows the first number. The second colour band is the second number. The third colour band is the number of '0's after the first two numbers.

Colour		Number
Black		0
Brown		1
Red		2
Orange		3
Yellow		4
Green		5
Blue		6
Violet		7
Grey		8
White		9

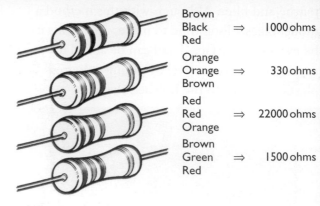

Brown Black Red	⇒	1000 ohms
Orange Orange Brown	⇒	330 ohms
Red Red Orange	⇒	22000 ohms
Brown Green Red	⇒	1500 ohms

Resistor colour code examples

Components and Symbols

Each type of component in an electric circuit has a symbol to represent it in a circuit diagram.

Name of component	Picture of component	Symbol
Resistor		
Wire		
Cell		
Switch		
Light Dependent Resistor		
Light Emitting Diode		
Bulb		

Some basic circuits for simple projects

Automatic light

This circuit will turn a light on if somebody stands on the door mat.

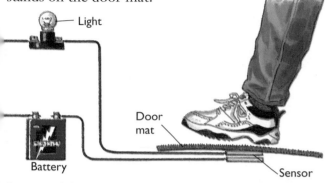

Automatic light

How it works

If there is nobody on the mat, the switch under the mat will be open. There is no route for the electricity to move around the circuit. Electric current will not flow and the bulb will not light. If somebody stands on the mat, there is a complete circuit and current will flow through the bulb, making it light up. The switch under the mat is made out of cardboard and aluminium foil.

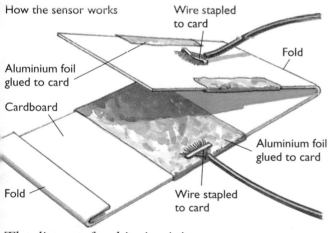

The diagram for this circuit is:

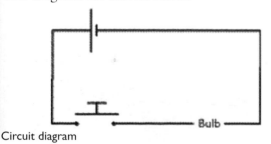

Circuit diagram

With a little inventiveness this circuit can be made to light a bulb when a box lid is opened, just like a car door light. You need to make a switch which closes when the lid opens.

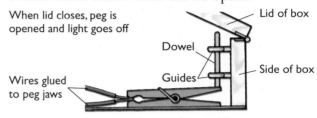

If the bulb is swapped for a buzzer, the circuit can become an alarm to tell you that somebody has opened the box!

Using an LED

An LED, or light emitting diode, is a small light which glows when very small amounts of electric current flow through it. The leg next to the flat on the LED is connected to the − side of the circuit, the other leg is connected to the + side. The LED also needs a resistor with it, to limit the current that flows. Use a 1000 ohm resistor with a supply between 5 and 10 volts.

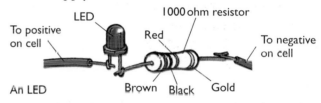

An LED

Questions

1 Glass is an insulator, gold is a conductor. Which of these will let electricity flow easily?

2 All metals conduct electricity well. Make a list of ten metals.

3 What is the colour code for these resistors?
   a 220
   b 47
   c 3300
   d 100000
   e 1500000.

4 What resistor has a colour code of brown, green, red?

Printed circuit boards and soldering

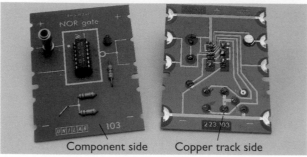

Printed circuit boards

Component side   Copper track side

Printed circuit boards are used to connect electronic components together. The copper tracks on the back of the board are like wires which transport electric current from one part of the circuit to another.

Making a PCB (printed circuit board)

Stage 1 Design

A circuit diagram shows how the components fit together:

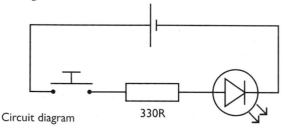

Circuit diagram   330R

The actual positions and distances between the contacts on each component are researched.

Resistor   LED

The positions of the components and the route for the copper track is laid out.

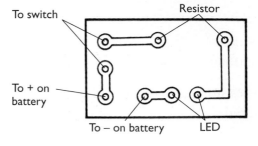

To switch   Resistor

To + on battery

To – on battery   LED

Because the components are on one side of the board and the copper is on the other, the layout of the tracks needs to be reversed.

The track layout is the mirror image of the component layout

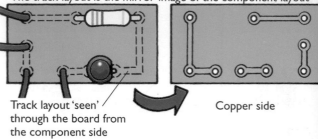

Track layout 'seen' through the board from the component side

Copper side

Stage 2 Making

- The copper surface of the board is cleaned using wire wool.
- A permanent marker or transfers are used to mark the route of each copper track. The ink is called etch resist because it protects the copper from being etched.
- The board is placed in a tank with a chemical which removes the copper layer. This is called etching. Where the track marks are, the liquid cannot etch the copper, so the copper under the ink is not removed.
- The board is removed from the tank and washed.
- Wire wool is used to remove the etch resist marks.
- Holes are drilled in the board for the component legs to fit through.

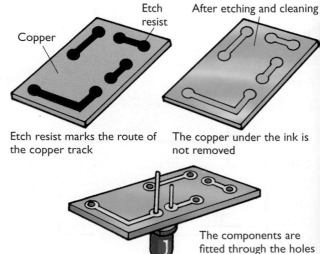

Copper   Etch resist   After etching and cleaning

Etch resist marks the route of the copper track   The copper under the ink is not removed

The components are fitted through the holes

Solder

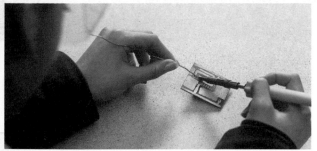

Soldering a joint

Electronic components are normally joined together using solder. Solder is an alloy of several metals. It has quite a low melting point.

Making a solder joint

1 Protective clothing must be worn.
2 Wear eye protectors.

Soldering uses hot equipment. The soldering iron should be placed in a stand which usually has a small piece of damp sponge for cleaning the tip of the soldering iron.

Make sure that the surfaces to be soldered are clean.

If a PCB is being used, push the legs through the holes and bend the legs along the copper track. This makes the joint physically strong.

The joint is made stronger

If a component is being soldered to a wire, a small hook can be formed in the end of the wire.

A small hook can be formed

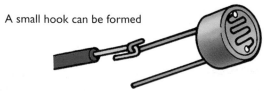

Using a clean soldering iron bit, touch the tip of the bit with some solder. This will 'wet' the bit and make it easier for heat to flow. Place the tip of the soldering iron against the two surfaces to be joined.

It is important that both surfaces are hot before solder is used. After a few seconds put the solder against the metal *not the soldering iron*. Solder will flow into the gap between the two surfaces and bond with them.

A good solder joint is volcano-shaped because the solder has flowed along the surfaces. If the surfaces were not hot enough then the solder forms a ball, and the join will be poor. If the soldering iron is left on the work too long, the copper track may lift off the board and the component may be damaged.

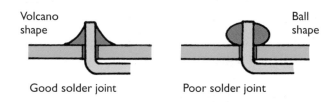

Volcano shape   Ball shape

Good solder joint   Poor solder joint

The electronics industry uses photographic methods to put the etch resist on the copper boards. Soldering is usually done by machine.

To do

1 Create a display showing the design of a printed circuit board. Explain why it is important to make the holes in a PCB the right distance apart.

2 Using words and diagrams, explain why the pattern of tracks for joining components has to be reversed before being used on the copper side of the board.

3 Plan a PCB layout for the circuit below.

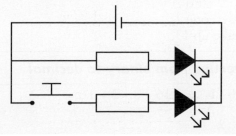

Logic, digital and binary counting

Digital micro-electronics is the technology that controls all the important systems in our modern society. The individual building blocks used are very simple to understand but they can be put together in very complicated systems like a computer. The binary logic explained in this section can be used to control simple projects like an automatic light-activated alarm with a manual switch.

Binary counting

Binary is a counting system using only 1 and 0. The normal counting system is decimal, using 0 1 2 3 4 5 6 7 8 9.

In the decimal system each column is ten times bigger than the column on its right.

```
 263                ⌐×10  ⌐×10  ⌐×10
= 200              | 100 | 10 | 1 |
 +60               |  2  |  6 | 3 |
 +  3              |     |    |   |
```

In the binary system each column is two times bigger than the column on its right.

```
                    ⌐×2   ⌐×2   ⌐×2
 1010              | 8 | 4 | 2 | 1 |
                   | 1 | 0 | 1 | 0 |
```

Converting from decimal to binary

13 = 8 + 4 + 1	8	4	2	1
There is one 8	1	1	0	1
one 4				
no 2				
one 1				
to make up 13				

Converting from binary to decimal

```
 1 1 0 1 1   =  16 + 8 + 2 + 1
 ↗ ↑  ↑ ↑ ↖  =  27
16 8  2 1
```

Counting in binary

Decimal number	Binary number			
	8	4	2	1
0	0	0	0	0
1	0	0	0	1
2	0	0	1	0
3	0	0	1	1
4	0	1	0	0
5	0	1	0	1
6	0	1	1	0
7	0	1	1	1
8	1	0	0	0
9	1	0	0	1

Digital signals

Digital signals use the binary system of counting. They are made up of 1 and 0. A light sensor can detect light or dark. If it is light, the light sensor will give out a '1'. If it is dark, the light sensor will give out a '0'.

Computers and telephones use digital signals to send messages, because the information that is received is always accurate.

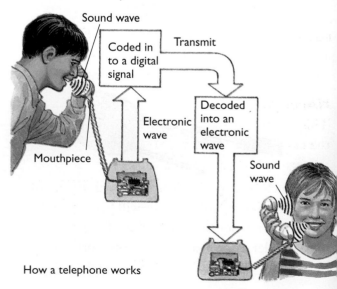

How a telephone works

Logic

Logic is an electronic way of making decisions. The small electronic circuits that make decisions are called logic gates. Logic gates use the binary counting system.

A logic gate has three parts: input, process and output. The inputs and outputs are labelled using letters. The process is labelled using a description of what it does. There are many types of logic gate, but the basic ones are:

AND gate

The output is a 1 when A AND B are 1.

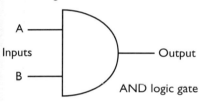

A B	Out
0 0	0
0 1	0
1 0	0
1 1	1

OR gate

The output is a 1 when A OR B is 1.

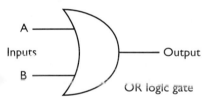

A B	Out
0 0	0
0 1	1
1 0	1
1 1	1

NOT gate

The output is NOT the input. If the input is 1 then the output is NOT 1 so it is 0.

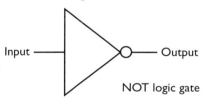

In	Out
0	1
1	0

NAND gate

This is similar to an AND gate, but the output is the opposite, i.e. when an AND gate would give a 1 the NAND gate gives a 0.

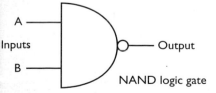

A B	Out
0 0	1
0 1	1
1 0	1
1 1	0

NOR gate

This is similar to an OR gate but the output is the opposite, i.e. when an OR gate would give a 1 a NOR gate will give a 0.

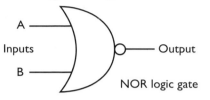

A B	Out
0 0	1
0 1	0
1 0	0
1 1	0

Logic gates in systems

Logic gates can be used as the process part of a system.

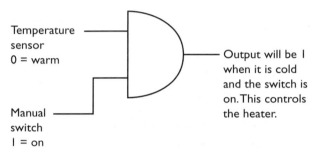

Two or more logic gates can be put together to make more complicated decisions.

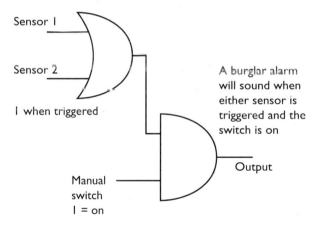

To do

1. Make a chart which shows the binary and decimal numbers up to 15.

2. Convert these decimal numbers to binary: 6 13 27 104.

3. Convert the binary number 10110 to decimal.

Systems, CAM and CAD

Systems

A system has three main parts: input, process and output. The three parts are often represented as a block diagram.

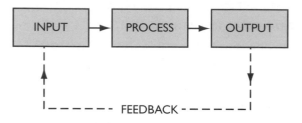

Feedback is the fourth element of a system.

To understand what a system is, think about the temperature control in a central heating system.

- The input to this system is the thermostat, which tells the system if it is too cold or too hot.

- The process is the decision-making part. If it is too cold, the heater must be turned on. If it is too hot, the heater must be turned off.

- The output is the boiler control.

- Feedback is when the air heats up because the heater has been on and the thermostat tells the system that it is now too hot.

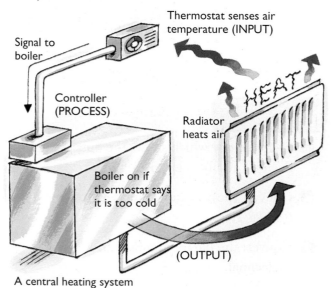

A central heating system

This system is designed to keep the temperature of a room even. What temperature it stays at depends on how the sensor is set. The system can become far more complicated if timers are added to allow heating only during the day.

Manufacturing companies making all sorts of products use many complicated systems. Some of these are part of the making process, others are to do with training, quality control, etc.

Robot arms

Moving parts from one place to another is a task which is easy for a computer to control. A robot arm can be used to pick up objects. The computer gives instructions to the robot arm, and sensors on the arm send information back to the computer telling it when the arm has moved into place.

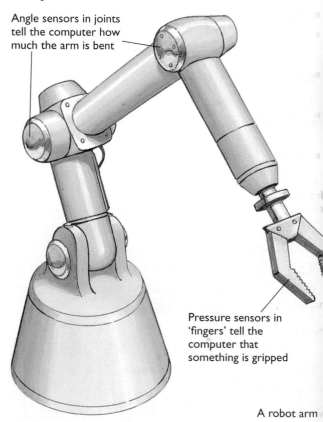

A robot arm

CAM

Computer controlled robot arms manufacturing cars

CAM stands for computer-aided manufacture.

CAM means that some of the making is done using computers to control the equipment. For example, a computer can control a robotic arm.

CAM has some advantages:

- Computers do not get tired.
- Computers do not make mistakes if programmed properly.
- Computers can control several machines at one time.
- Computer-controlled production gives very reliable standards of manufacture.
- Computers can control the movement of parts to different machines.

Information to store

Orders to suppliers

Stock checks

...ation

...uction

Will computers replace people?

CAD

CAD stands for computer-aided design. Many designers use computers to help them design products. Some of the advantages of using computers are:

- Computers can be used to make changes very quickly.
- Computers can be used to produce drawings very accurately and change them without the need to redraw plans.
- Computers can produce views of three-dimensional objects without the need to make them.
- Computers can show (simulate) how an object will behave without expensive testing.
- Computers make information available from across the world.
- Lots of information can be stored reliably using very little space.

Lots of information can be stored using very little space

To do

1 Write down a list of all the electronic systems you can think of that you use during the day.

2 Find out how an electric iron works and draw the block diagram for the system.

Information technology

IT in business

The use of information technology (IT) in business has changed the way that products are made and sold.

Computers have had a big impact on:

Design – many designs now include 'onboard computers' to control how a system works. For example, some cars have computers built into them to improve the way that the engine runs.

Designing – A computer can model designs and show you very quickly what something will look like or how it will behave without you actually having to make it.

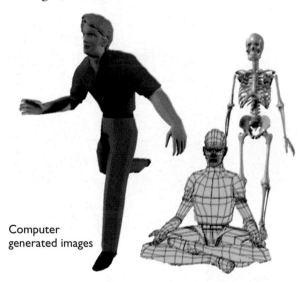

Computer generated images

Making – when a computer replaces people in the production process, the savings in labour reduce the manufacturing costs. Many of the household items you use would be far more expensive if it were not for the computer which controlled the production.

Organization – computers can keep an eye on all the stages of a production line, and give early warning of problems. The computer can also order parts automatically from suppliers.

Stock control – almost all businesses now control their stock by computer. The bar code system is used to make a record of what is sold. The computer can then tell the staff when and what to replace on the shelves. In some supermarkets the computer decides when more stock must be ordered, so that they never run out.

A portable barcode scanner

Quality control – an automatic testing system can test a complicated product extremely quickly, and if the same fault keeps happening, it will tell the production manager of the problem.

Money – computers are ideal for keeping track of finances and whether bills have been paid.

When is it worth using a computer?

Almost all companies use computers for their finance and office systems. (In manufacture, installation (setting up) costs can be too high.)

The main advantage of humans over computers is their ability to learn, which makes humans more adaptable than computers.

"So that's why the computer can't do it!"

IT in design and technology

Information technology has changed the way people learn.

- Computers can store enormous amounts of information, and it can be found almost immediately.
- It is very simple to search a computer's memory for information on any subject.
- Links between computers on the internet allow people to research using knowledge from the whole world.

IT for students

There are many areas where computers can be used by students:

Spreadsheets – a spreadsheet is a chart showing lots of information. Computers are able to store this information and calculate, using equations. It is very simple to create graphs and charts from the information in a spreadsheet.

Spreadsheet screen

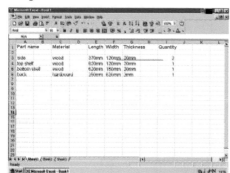

Databases – a database is a way of storing information so that different pieces of information can be compared. A search through a school register database could, for example, find all the pupils with a birthday in March, who also live in a particular area.

Research – CD-ROMs can hold enormous quantities of information including sounds and video. The Internet allows you to search the memory of computer systems across the world. This makes it possible for you to research using more information than is contained in any one library.

Word processing – a word processor is used to produce written documents. Because the computer holds information electronically, it is very easy to correct mistakes, or to add or take away text, without rewriting a whole page.

Desktop publishing – a desktop publishing package is used to create pages with pictures and text on them like a printed book. This can make your work attractive to the reader.

Drawing – drawing on a computer is very quick and good looking graphics can be created with little artistic skill.

Control – computers can be used to control movement, sound and light. They can also sense physical changes to the environment, including temperature, brightness and humidity, allowing the computer to control a system.

Computer controlled robot arm

To do

1. Find out the number of pupils in your class that were born in each month. Put this information on to a spreadsheet. Use a bar chart on the computer to display this information.

2. Gather information about deforestation in the Amazon jungle. Produce a single sheet containing key points. You should include a short comment of your own on the issue.

Pneumatics

Safety

Pneumatic systems are dangerous, as a blast of air under pressure, or a small part being shot out of a pipe, can easily harm someone.

The correct eye protection must always be worn to prevent injury.

Pneumatics

Pneumatics is the use of air under pressure to move things. When you pump up a tyre, air is being forced out of the pump and into the tyre. Imagine connecting two bicycle pumps together: as one pump handle is pushed in, the other will be forced out.

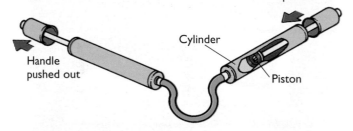

The moving part of the pump is called the piston. The tube in which the piston moves is called the cylinder.

Parts of pneumatic systems

There are many types of valve, but they all control the movement of air.

One-way valve – only allows air to flow in one direction. As air tries to flow back, the air pressure shuts the valve.

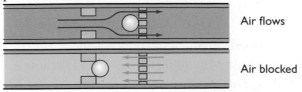

A one-way valve

Single action cylinder – the simplest moving part of a pneumatic system. If air is forced into the cylinder the piston moves, and when air is let out again the spring moves the piston back.

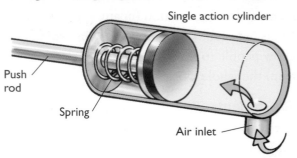

Three port valve – can control the flow of air into and out of the cylinder. If the button is pressed, air will flow into the cylinder and push the piston out. When the button is not pressed, the air supply is cut off and the spring pushes air back out of the cylinder. A single action cylinder and three port valve could be used to crush cans at a recycling centre. The large force is needed to crush the can, but only a small force is needed to bring the piston back up.

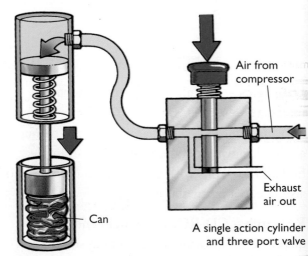

A single action cylinder and three port valve

Double action cylinder – used where a large force is needed in both directions. If air is let into one end, the piston moves one way; if air is let into the other end it moves back. Doors can be opened and closed in this way.

Pressure, force and area

Pressure is a measure of how much force (measured in Newtons) pushes on an area (square metres).

If a force of 30 Newtons pushes on an area of two square metres, then the pressure is 15 Newtons per square metre.

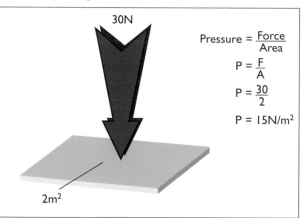

$$\text{Pressure} = \frac{\text{Force}}{\text{Area}}$$

$$P = \frac{F}{A}$$

$$P = \frac{30}{2}$$

$$P = 15\text{N/m}^2$$

The air pressure on your body at this moment is about 100 000 Newtons per square metre.

When pressurized air is let into a cylinder, it pushes on the piston. The force on the piston is bigger if the area of the piston is larger. The drawback is that the larger the area of the piston, the slower the piston will move.

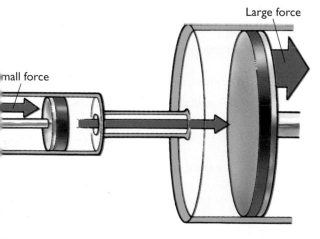

The force on the small piston gives a much larger force on the large piston, but the large piston will not move very far:

$$\text{small force} \times \text{large movement} = \text{large force} \times \text{small movement}$$

Pneumatics in use

Pneumatic systems can create very large forces without the need for gears and chains. The pneumatics components can be attached anywhere on a machine and the flexible tubes that carry the air to the cylinders can go around corners.

Pneumatics are often used in manufacturing to quickly grip and move objects about. This is because pneumatic systems move quickly, and the valves are easily controlled by a computer or an automatic system. An electrical system to do the same job would be very expensive and would not deliver the same forces.

Lorry air brakes are driven by compressed air. The noisy hiss you hear when a lorry moves off is the air escaping from the cylinders in the brake system.

Questions

1 What is the pressure in these three examples?

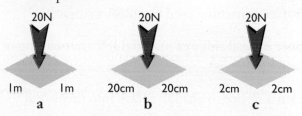

2 The two syringe pistons below are connected by a flexible tube. The area of the larger syringe is twice the area of the smaller one. If the smaller one is pushed all the way in, how far will the large syringe piston move?

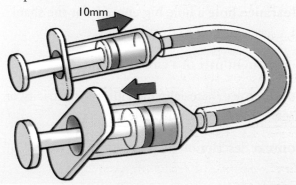

Glossary

abrasive used to rub the surface of a material to make it smooth

alloy a mixture of two or more metals

analyse to study closely

applications ways of using something

automated carried out by machine without the need for people

batch production where a number of items are made at the same time

biodegradable a material which naturally breaks down into harmless chemicals

brainstorm a way of generating lots of ideas

brief a short statement of a problem

buffer a machine used to polish a surface

burr a small ridge of material left after cutting or drilling

cam a device to change rotary into reciprocal movement

capital energy energy sources which cannot be renewed

chamfer taking the corner off the square edge of a piece of material

clearance hole a hole big enough for the shank of a screw or bolt to fit through

component part of a circuit or system

conductor a material which allows electricity or heat to move easily through it

context description of a situation

continuous production when products are made one after another

crank a device for turning rotary movement into reciprocal movement

criteria requirements of a project

cross-section imaginary view through an object

crude oil oil from underground before refining

deciduous trees ones which lose all their leaves in winter

development the process of taking design ideas and making them into a final design

disassemble to study a product closely and work out how and why it was made

distorted bent out of shape

dowel solid wooden cylinder often used in joints

economical financially worth doing

emery cloth fabric with small hard grains stuck to it; used to smooth metals

evaluation comparing the outcome of something with what was asked for in the specification

flush when two surfaces are level

flux substance used to make solder flow

format way of presenting information

former device to help bend material into shape

friction force between two surfaces resisting movement

generating a brief a short written statement of the problem to be solved

grain the light and dark lines in wood

insulator does not conduct heat or electric current

isometric style of three-dimensional drawing

justify to give reasons for choices

key features important points of a design

linear movement in a straight line

MDF medium density fibreboard

maintenance planned servicing

managed forest one which is maintained to produce a continuous supply of timber

manufacture the process of making

manufactured boards plywood, hardboard, chipboard and MDF

market research identifying needs and opportunities

mass production making items in large quantities

metal ore rock from which metals can be taken out

modifications changes to a design

moulding material with a complicated cross-section. Also forming a material by putting it into a mould

ohm unit of electrical resistance

orthographic a system of drawing where objects are looked at from different directions

perspective three-dimensional system of drawing producing realistic views

pilot hole small hole used to guide a screw or thread

pinion gear wheel used with a rack

planed made smooth by a tool called a plane

process a sequence of operations

prototype a development model

proud surface which is raised above another

quality assurance system used to make sure products are made correctly

quality control system of testing to check that products meet standards that are set out

rack and pinion device for changing rotary to linear movement

raw material material that has not been changed in any way from its natural state; unprocessed

renewable a source of material or energy that can be replaced within a few years

rotary movement in a circle

rust when iron or steel waste away (corrode)

sketch a freehand drawing

source where information or material come from

specification a list of criteria

summary a statement of the main points

template shape used for marking out

tolerance the acceptable margin of error

tough a material which is difficult to break

vanishing point in perspective drawing, where construction lines meet

warp unwanted bending of wood as it dries

worm drive a spiral thread

Index